THEORETICAL MODELS FOR NUCLEAR ASTROPHYSICS

THEORETICAL MODELS FOR NUCLEAR ASTROPHYSICS

P. DESCOUVEMONT

Nova Science Publishers, Inc.
New York

Senior Editors: Susan Boriotti and Donna Dennis
Coordinating Editor: Tatiana Shohov
Office Manager: Annette Hellinger
Graphics: Wanda Serrano
Editorial Production: Vladimir Klestov, Matthew Kozlowski, Tom Moceri, Alexandra Columbus and Maya Columbus
Circulation: Ave Maria Gonzalez, Vera Popovic, Luis Aviles, Raymond Davis, Melissa Diaz, Marlene Nunez and Jeannie Pappas
Communications and Acquisitions: Serge P. Shohov
Marketing: Cathy DeGregory

Library of Congress Cataloging-in-Publication Data
Available upon request

ISBN 1-59033-856-1

Printed in the United States of America

Contents

Preface

We present different models used in nuclear astrophysics to derive charged-particle induced cross sections and reaction rates. We focus on reactions between light elements, such as those involved in the CNO cycle or in He burning. First, a general overview of the main reactions required for stellar evolution is presented. A discussion of the different types of reactions (transfer and capture reactions) is illustrated by some examples. Differences between resonant and non-resonant processes are pointed out. We start from general properties of scattering theory and present general formulas for capture and transfer cross sections. Then, we develop more specifically the potential and R-matrix models, often used in the literature, and we apply them to some typical reactions such as $^{12}C(p,\gamma)^{13}N$ and $^{3}He(\alpha, \gamma)^{7}Be$. Other direct (microscopic models, Distorted Wave Born Approximation theory) or indirect (Coulomb breakup, Asymptotic Normalization Constant) methods are briefly presented. The use of spectroscopic factors, widespread in nuclear astrophysics, and more generally in low-energy nuclear physics, is discussed. Finally we consider the calculation of reaction rates. For non-resonant reactions, we compare the standard analytical approach with the exact numerical treatment. Resonant reaction rates are illustrated by the $^{12}C(p,\gamma)^{13}N$ reaction.

Chapter 1

Introduction

Nuclear reactions essentially play two roles in stellar evolution [1]: the released energy compensates the gravitational contraction of the star, and nuclear reactions lead to the nucleosynthesis of elements [2]. The hypothesis of a pp chain, producing ^{4}He from four protons, was suggested in the 30's, but the grounds of modern nucleosynthesis were established by Burbidge *et al.* [3], in a paper referred to as B^{2}FH. These authors suggested different mechanisms to explain the nucleosynthesis of heavy elements: triple-α process, H and ^{4}He combustion and s, r and p processes. Recent reviews about stellar nucleosynthesis can be found in refs [4, 5, 6, 7]. Compilations on nuclear cross sections are also available [8, 9, 10].

The main problem encountered by B^{2}FH was a very poor knowledge of the nuclear reaction rates. It is well known that stellar energies are much lower than the Coulomb barrier and, consequently, the cross sections involving charged particles are very small, often unaccessible to experiment [11]. On the other hand, several stellar scenarios involve short-lived nuclei which are difficult to produce with high intensities [12, 13, 14].

In spite of impressive developments of experimental techniques, the determination of nuclear cross sections at stellar energies requires theoretical support. Some models, such as the R-matrix [15, 16] or the K-matrix [17] approaches, aim at fitting available experimental data, and extrapolating them down to stellar energies. Of course, these models require experimental information, such as elastic-scattering cross sections or spectroscopic properties. Others methods, such as the potential model [18, 19] or microscopic models [20, 21] rely on the wave functions of the system. In principle they do not need any experimental data, but in practice those data are used to constrain some parameters, or to test the

1

validity of the model.

The above-mentioned theories cannot be applied to high-energy reactions and to high-level densities, which should be treated by statistical models, such as the Hauser-Feshbach theory [22]. In this paper, we present a brief overview of different models widely used in nuclear astrophysics. We limit ourselves to low-level densities and we refer the reader to refs [22, 6] for details about high-level densities, which occur in reactions involving heavy isotopes (typically $A > 20$). We discuss the potential model, and the R-matrix method which can be applied very easily. We also present recent progress in other directions, such as microscopic models, or indirect methods.

In sect. 2, we present a general discussion of the cross sections. A definition of stellar energies is given, and we emphasize important properties of the Coulomb functions, which govern the cross sections at low energies. Radiative-capture and transfer cross sections are defined and the corresponding selection rules are illustrated by some examples. Section 3 deals with the potential model which is applied to radiative-capture reactions. The R-matrix method is presented in sect. 4 along with some examples of radiative-capture and transfer cross sections. Other models are discussed in sect. 5. Finally, sect. 6 is devoted to the calculation of reaction rates.

Chapter 2

Overview of Cross Sections

2.1 Stellar Energies

First, we must specify stellar energies, where the cross section needs to be known to evaluate the reaction rate. Let us consider a reaction between two nuclei with masses $A_1 m_N$ and $A_2 m_N$ and charges $Z_1 e$ and $Z_2 e$ (we express here the masses in units of the nuclear mass m_N, taken as the average value of the proton and neutron masses). The theory of stellar evolution involves the reaction rate at temperature T, defined as

$$N_A <\sigma v> \;=\; N_A \left(\frac{8}{\pi \mu m_N (k_B T)^3} \right)^{\frac{1}{2}} \int \sigma(E)\, E \, \exp(-E/k_B T)\, dE, \quad (2.1.1)$$

where we assume that the star can be considered as a perfect gas following the Maxwell-Boltzmann distribution. In eq. (2.1.1), v is the relative velocity, N_A is Avogadro's number, μ is the dimensionless reduced mass, and k_B is Boltzmann's constant. At sub-coulomb energies the cross section varies as

$$\sigma(E) \sim \exp(-2\pi\eta)/E, \quad (2.1.2)$$

where η is the Sommerfeld parameter

$$\eta = \frac{Z_1 Z_2 e^2}{\hbar v}. \quad (2.1.3)$$

Using (2.1.2), the integrand of (2.1.1) can be approximated by a Gaussian shape [8, 2] with a maximum at the Gamow peak energy

$$
\begin{aligned}
E_0 \;&=\; \left[\pi \frac{e^2}{\hbar c} Z_1 Z_2 k_B T (\mu m_N c^2/2)^{1/2} \right]^{2/3} \\
&\approx\; 0.122\, \mu^{1/3} (Z_1 Z_2 T_9)^{2/3} \text{ MeV}, \quad (2.1.4)
\end{aligned}
$$

and a width at $1/e$ height

$$\Delta E_0 = 4(E_0 k_B T/3)^{\frac{1}{2}}$$
$$\approx 0.237 \, (Z_1^2 Z_2^2 \mu)^{1/6} \, T_9^{5/6} \text{ MeV}, \qquad (2.1.5)$$

where T_9 is the temperature expressed in $10^9 K$. The Gamow energy defines the energy range where the cross section needs to be known to derive the reaction rate. In most cases, this energy is much lower than the Coulomb barrier which means that the cross sections drop to very low values. To compensate the fast energy dependence of the cross section, nuclear astrophysicists usually use the S-factor defined as

$$S(E) = \sigma(E) \, E \, \exp(2\pi\eta), \qquad (2.1.6)$$

which is mainly sensitive to the nuclear contribution to the cross section. For non-resonant reactions, the energy dependence of the S factor is smooth.

2.2   Scattering Wave Functions

There are essentially two types of reactions in astrophysical applications: radiative capture reactions, where the colliding nuclei fuse with a photon emission, and transfer reactions, where some nucleons are exchanged. To derive the cross sections, we need to define the scattering wave functions [23], common to both processes.

Let us consider two nuclei with spins and parity $(I_1\pi_1)$ and $(I_2\pi_2)$, and mass and charge numbers (A_1, Z_1), (A_2, Z_2). The hamiltonian reads

$$H = \sum_{i=1}^{A} T_i + \sum_{i<j=1}^{A} V_{ij}, \qquad (2.2.7)$$

where A is the total nucleon number $(A = A_1 + A_2)$, T_i is the kinetic energy of nucleon i, and V_{ij} a nucleon-nucleon interaction. If the relative coordinate ρ between the nuclei is large, the hamiltonian (2.2.7) can be approximated as

$$H \underset{\rho \to \infty}{\sim} H_1 + H_2 + T_{cm} + T_\rho + \frac{Z_1 Z_2 e^2}{\rho}, \qquad (2.2.8)$$

where T_{cm} and T_ρ are the center-of-mass and relative kinetic energies, and (H_1, H_2) the hamiltonians of nuclei 1 and 2. These internal hamiltonians provide the energies and wave functions

$$H_i \phi_i^{I_i \pi_i \nu_i}(\boldsymbol{\xi_i}) = E_i^{I_i \pi_i} \phi_i^{I_i \pi_i \nu_i}(\boldsymbol{\xi_i}), \tag{2.2.9}$$

$\boldsymbol{\xi_i}$ being the set of internal coordinates associated with nucleus i.

Coming back to the A-body problem, the asymptotic behavior [23] of the scattering wave function at center-of-mass energy E and with spin states $(I_1 \nu_1)$ and $(I_2 \nu_2)$ in the entrance channel is given by [1]

$$\Psi^{\nu_1 \nu_2}(\boldsymbol{k}) \to \frac{1}{\sqrt{v}} \sum_{\nu_1' \nu_2'} \phi^{I_1 \pi_1 \nu_1'} \phi^{I_2 \pi_2 \nu_2'} \tag{2.2.10}$$

$$\left(\exp(i\boldsymbol{k}.\boldsymbol{\rho}) \delta_{\nu_1 \nu_1'} \delta_{\nu_2 \nu_2'} + f_{\nu_1 \nu_2, \nu_1' \nu_2'}(\theta) \exp(ik\rho)/\rho \right),$$

where k is the wave number

$$k = (2\mu m_N E/\hbar^2)^{1/2}, \tag{2.2.11}$$

θ is the scattering angle and $f(\theta)$ the scattering amplitude. The $v^{-1/2}$ factor ensures the normalization to a unit flux. In eq. (2.2.11), we have neglected the Coulomb potential for the sake of clarity, but the calculations are not affected by this approximation. On the other hand, inelastic channels have not been explicitly written; a generalization is straightforward but makes the presentation more complicated.

In practice the scattering wave function is expanded in partial waves as

$$\Psi^{\nu_1 \nu_2}(\boldsymbol{k}) = \sum_{JM\pi\ell I} \sqrt{\frac{4\pi}{2\ell+1}} < I_1 I_2 \nu_1 \nu_2 | I \nu >$$

$$< \ell I m \nu | J M > \Psi_{\ell I}^{JM\pi} Y_\ell^{m*}(\Omega_k), \tag{2.2.12}$$

where different quantum numbers show up: the channel spin I, the relative angular momentum ℓ, the total spin J and the total parity $\pi = \pi_1 \pi_2 (-)^\ell$. Since the hamiltonian (2.2.8) is split in terms acting in different spaces, the asymptotic wave functions can be factored by using the channel wave function

$$\varphi_{\ell I}^{JM\pi}(\Omega_\rho, \boldsymbol{\xi_1}, \boldsymbol{\xi_2}) = \left[Y_\ell(\Omega_\rho) \otimes [\phi_1^{I_1 \pi_1}(\boldsymbol{\xi_1}) \otimes \phi_2^{I_2 \pi_2}(\boldsymbol{\xi_2})]^I \right]^{JM}. \tag{2.2.13}$$

Expanding eq. (2.2.11) in the same way as eq. (2.2.12) we have

$$\Psi_{\ell I}^{JM\pi} \xrightarrow[\rho \to \infty]{} \sum_{\ell' I'} g_{\ell I, \ell' I'}^{J\pi, as}(\rho) \, \varphi_{\ell' I'}^{JM\pi}(\Omega_\rho, \boldsymbol{\xi_1}, \boldsymbol{\xi_2}), \tag{2.2.14}$$

---

[1]Throughout this paper, E is the c.m. energy defined with respect to the two-body threshold $E_1 + E_2$

where the asymptotic relative function $g^{J\pi,as}(\rho)$ is a solution of the Coulomb equation

$$\left[\frac{-\hbar^2}{2\mu m_N}\left(\frac{d^2}{d\rho^2}+\frac{2}{\rho}\frac{d}{d\rho}-\frac{\ell(\ell+1)}{\rho^2}\right)+\right.$$

$$\left.\frac{Z_1Z_2e^2}{\rho}-E g^{J\pi,as}_{\ell I,\ell'I'}(\rho)\right]=0,$$

$$(2.2.15)$$

and is written as

$$g^{J\pi,as}_{\ell I,\ell'I'}(\rho)=i^{\ell+1}(\pi(2\ell+1)/v)^{1/2}$$

$$\left[I_\ell(k\rho)\delta_{\ell\ell'}\delta_{II'}-U^{J\pi}_{\ell I,\ell'I'}O_\ell(k\rho)\right]/k\rho. \qquad (2.2.16)$$

In eq. (2.2.16), I_ℓ and O_ℓ are the incoming and outgoing Coulomb functions (see next subsection), and $U^{J\pi}$ is the collision matrix which contains the information about the collision. This matrix is symmetric and unitary [23]. The amplitude of the relative wave function is consistent with the unit-flux normalization of the scattering state (2.2.11).

For closed channels ($E < 0$), the solution of eq. (2.2.15) is a Whittaker function [24] which tends to zero at large distances; we have

$$g^{J\pi,as}_{\ell I,\ell'I'}(\rho)=C^{J\pi}_{\ell I,\ell'I'}W_{-\eta,\ell+\frac{1}{2}}(2k\rho)/\rho, \qquad (2.2.17)$$

where C is the so-called "asymptotic normalization constant" (ANC).

2.3   Coulomb Functions

Since the cross sections at stellar energies are governed by the Coulomb interaction, the properties of Coulomb functions are quite important. We briefly mention their main properties. For positive energies ($E > 0$), eq. (2.2.15) is rewritten as

$$\frac{d^2g_\ell}{dx^2}+\left(1-\frac{2\eta}{x}-\frac{\ell(\ell+1)}{x^2}\right)g_\ell=0, \qquad (2.3.18)$$

which has the regular (F_ℓ) and irregular (G_ℓ) functions as solution. The incoming and outgoing functions I_ℓ and O_ℓ are defined as

$$I_\ell(x)=O^*_\ell(x)=e^{i\omega_\ell}\left(G_\ell(x,\eta)-iF_\ell(x,\eta)\right), \qquad (2.3.19)$$

where the Coulomb phase shift is

$$\omega_\ell = \sum_{s=1}^{\ell} \arctan \frac{\eta}{s}. \qquad (2.3.20)$$

Traditionally, the η dependence of I_ℓ and O_ℓ is not explicitly written. At low energies, it can be shown [25, 26] that

$$F_\ell(x, \eta) \longrightarrow \sqrt{\pi x} \, \exp(-\pi\eta) \, I_{2\ell+1}(x)$$
$$G_\ell(x, \eta) \longrightarrow \sqrt{4x/\pi} \, \exp(\pi\eta) \, K_{2\ell+1}(x), \qquad (2.3.21)$$

where $I_{2\ell+1}(x)$ and $K_{2\ell+1}(x)$ are the modified Bessel functions. The dependence on x and η can be therefore factored. Equations (2.3.21) show that F_ℓ decreases with energy while G_ℓ diverges when energy tends to zero.

For negative energies, eq. (2.2.15) reduces to

$$\frac{d^2 g_\ell}{dx^2} - \left(1 + \frac{2\eta}{x} + \frac{\ell(\ell+1)}{x^2}\right) g_\ell = 0, \qquad (2.3.22)$$

whose solution is the Whittaker function

$$g_\ell(x) = W_{-\eta, \ell+1/2}(2x), \qquad (2.3.23)$$

with the asymptotic behavior

$$W_{-\eta, \ell+1/2}(x) \longrightarrow \exp(-x/2)/x^\eta. \qquad (2.3.24)$$

In many applications, one uses the constant

$$\begin{aligned} L_\ell &= ka \frac{O_\ell'(ka)}{O_\ell(ka)} = S_\ell(ka) + iP_\ell(ka) \text{ for } E \geq 0, \\ &= 2ka \frac{W_{-\eta, \ell+1/2}'(2ka)}{W_{-\eta, \ell+1/2}(2ka)} = S_\ell(ka) \text{ for } E \leq 0, \qquad (2.3.25) \end{aligned}$$

where a is a typical distance, for instance the sum of the nuclear radii. For positive energies, one derives the penetration factor P_ℓ and the shift factor S_ℓ

$$P_\ell(x) = x/[F_\ell^2(x) + G_\ell^2(x)]$$
$$S_\ell(x) = [F_\ell(x)F_\ell'(x) + G_\ell(x)G_\ell'(x)] \, P_\ell(x). \qquad (2.3.26)$$

At low energies eq.(2.3.21) shows that the penetration factor varies as

$$P_\ell(x) \sim \exp(-2\pi\eta), \tag{2.3.27}$$

and can be interpreted as the transmission probability through the Coulomb and centrifugal barriers. It decreases very rapidly when energy goes to zero. Let us point out that

- for negative energies, the penetration factor vanishes, and only S_ℓ can be defined.

- for neutron-induced reactions, we have $\eta = 0$, and the penetration factor varies as $k^{2\ell+1}$.

In fig.2.3.1, we present P_ℓ and S_ℓ for the $\alpha+{}^3$He and $\alpha+$n systems for $a = 5$ fm. As expected, the penetration factor strongly depends on energy for the charged system $\alpha+{}^3$He. Owing to the centrifugal barrier, it decreases with increasing ℓ. On the other hand, the shift factor smoothly depends on energy. The Thomas approximation, which will be used in the following, assumes that the energy dependence of S_ℓ is linear in a limited interval; this approximation is in general fairly accurate. For systems involving a neutron, the derivative of S_0 is discontinuous at $E = 0$, which needs special treatment.

2.4 Radiative Capture Cross Sections

Stellar scenarios involve many radiative capture reactions, such as (p, γ), (α, γ) or (n, γ). The cross sections are deduced from first-order perturbation theory, assuming that the photon-emission hamiltonian H_e is small compared with the nuclear hamiltonian (2.2.7). We briefly present here the main steps to derive the cross section; further details can be found in ref. [27].

In a capture process, two nuclei fuse which leads to a final state of the unified system with spin and parity J_f and π_f. If $\Psi^{J_f M_f \pi_f}$ is the wave function of the final state, the cross section reads

$$\frac{d\sigma_c}{d\Omega_\gamma}(E, J_f\pi_f) = \frac{k_\gamma}{2\pi\hbar} \frac{1}{(2I_1 + 1)(2I_2 + 1)} \tag{2.4.28}$$
$$\sum_{q\nu_1\nu_2 M_f} | < \Psi^{J_f M_f \pi_f}|H_e(q, \Omega_\gamma)|\Psi^{\nu_1\nu_2}(E) > |^2,$$

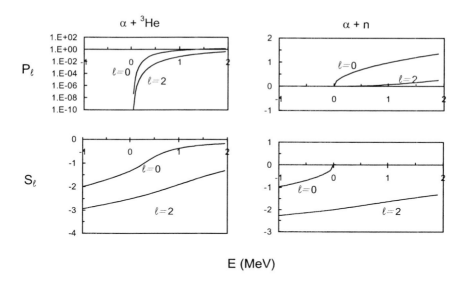

E (MeV)

Figure 2.3.1: *Functions P_ℓ and S_ℓ for the $\alpha + {}^3He$ and $\alpha + n$ systems for $a = 5$ fm.*

where the emitted photon is characterized by its wave number k_γ, emission angle Ω_γ, and polarization q. Energy conservation requires

$$E_\gamma = \hbar k_\gamma c = E - E_f, \qquad (2.4.29)$$

E_f being the (negative) final-state energy.

To develop eq. (2.4.29), we expand the electromagnetic hamiltonian H_e in electric (E) and magnetic (M) multipoles; we have

$$H_e(q, \Omega_\gamma) = \sum_{\sigma\lambda\mu} (-)^{\lambda+1} q^\sigma \alpha_\lambda^\sigma \mathcal{M}_{\lambda\mu}^\sigma \mathcal{D}_{\mu-q}^\lambda(\Omega_\gamma), \qquad (2.4.30)$$

where σ takes the values 0 or 1 (E or M) for the electric and magnetic multipoles [27], and $\mathcal{D}_{\mu-q}^\lambda(\Omega_\gamma)$ is a Wigner function. Constants α_λ^σ are given by

$$\alpha_\lambda^E = i\alpha_\lambda^M = \frac{(ik_\gamma)^\lambda}{(2\lambda+1)!!} \left[\frac{2\pi(\lambda+1)(2\lambda+1)}{\lambda} \right]^{\frac{1}{2}}. \qquad (2.4.31)$$

Using the long-wavelength approximation ($k_\gamma r \ll 1$, where r is a typical dimension of the system), the multipole operators read

$$\mathcal{M}_{\lambda\mu}^E = e \sum_i^A g_\ell(i) \, r_i^\lambda Y_\lambda^\mu(\Omega_{r_i})$$

$$\mathcal{M}_{\lambda\mu}^M = \mu_N \sum_i^A \left[\frac{2g_\ell(i)}{\lambda+1} \ell_i + g_s(i)s_i \right] \cdot \nabla r_i^\lambda Y_\lambda^\mu(\Omega_{r_i}), \quad (2.4.32)$$

where $\boldsymbol{\rho}_i$, $\boldsymbol{\ell}_i$ and $\boldsymbol{s}_i$ are the space coordinate, the orbital angular momentum and the spin of nucleon i, respectively, and μ_N is the Bohr magneton

$$\mu_N = \frac{e\hbar}{2m_N c}. \quad (2.4.33)$$

In (2.4.32), the operators $g_\ell(i)$ and $g_s(i)$ are defined in the isospin formalism as

$$g_\ell(i) = \frac{1}{2} - t_{i3}$$
$$g_s(i) = g_p(\frac{1}{2} - t_{i3}) + g_n(\frac{1}{2} + t_{i3}), \quad (2.4.34)$$

where t_i is the isospin of nucleon i, and g_p, g_n are the gyromagnetic factors of the proton ($g_p = 5.586$) and of the neutron ($g_n = -3.826$). Let us notice that definitions (2.4.32) also assume the Siegert approximation which is exact if the nuclear interaction does not depend on velocity, and if the wave functions are exact solutions of the Schrödinger equation (see ref. [27] for detail).

The matrix elements of the multipole operators satisfy the selection rules

$$|J_i - J_f| \leq \lambda \leq J_i + J_f$$
$$\pi_i \pi_f = (-)^{\sigma+\lambda}, \quad (2.4.35)$$

where $(J_i \pi_i)$ and $(J_f \pi_f)$ are the quantum numbers of the initial and find states, respectively. Another important selection rule concerns $E1$ transitions for $N = Z$ nuclei ($T_3 = 0$), where we must have

$$\Delta T = \pm 1, \quad (2.4.36)$$

which means that $E1$ transitions are forbidden in $N = Z$ nuclei, if isospin impurities are neglected.

Using expansions (2.4.30) and (2.2.12), the cross section (2.4.29) is written as

$$\frac{d\sigma_c}{d\Omega_\gamma}(E, J_f \pi_f) = \frac{2J_f + 1}{(2I_1 + 1)(2I_2 + 1)} \sum_j a_j(E) P_j(\cos\theta_\gamma), \quad (2.4.37)$$

where P_j is a Legendre polynomial, and $a_j(E)$ is defined by

$$a_j(E) = \frac{k_\gamma}{\hbar\pi} \sum_{\lambda\lambda'\sigma\sigma'}{}' \sum_{I\ell_iJ_i\ell_i'J_i'} (-)^{I-J_f+1} X^{\sigma\lambda}_{I\ell_iJ_i}(E) X^{\sigma'\lambda'*}_{I\ell_i'J_i'}(E)$$

$$\times < \ell_i\, 0\, \ell_i'\, 0 | j\, 0 > < \lambda -1\, \lambda'\, 1 | j\, 0 >$$

$$\left\{ \begin{array}{ccc} J_i & J_i' & j \\ \ell_i' & \ell_i & I \end{array} \right\} \left\{ \begin{array}{ccc} J_i & J_i' & j \\ \lambda' & \lambda & J_f \end{array} \right\}, \tag{2.4.38}$$

where notation Σ' means that the summation is limited by the condition $(-)^j = (-)^{\lambda+\lambda'+\sigma+\sigma'}$, and where

$$X^{\sigma\lambda}_{I\ell_iJ_i}(E) = \alpha^\sigma_\lambda (2J_i+1)^{\frac{1}{2}} < \Psi^{J_f\pi_f} || \mathcal{M}^\sigma_\lambda || \Psi^{J_i\pi_i}_{\ell_iI}(E) > . \tag{2.4.39}$$

Definition (2.4.37) does not depend on the model; it is valid for any theoretical model provided the normalization (2.2.16) of the scattering wave function is used. In general, one needs the total cross section, integrated over all photon directions. Integrating (2.4.37) provides

$$\sigma_c(E, J_f\pi_f) = \frac{2J_f+1}{(2I_1+1)(2I_2+1)} \sum_{\sigma\lambda J_i I\ell_i} \frac{k_\gamma^{2\lambda+1}}{2\ell_i+1} \frac{8\pi(\lambda+1)}{\hbar\lambda(2\lambda+1)!!^2} \tag{2.4.40}$$

$$| < \Psi^{J_f\pi_f} || \mathcal{M}^\sigma_\lambda || \Psi^{J_i\pi_i}_{\ell_iI}(E) > |^2.$$

In practice, the summation in (2.4.41) involves a few terms only. On one hand, selection rules (2.4.35) limit the $(J_i\pi_i)$ values. On the other hand, one multipole is in general dominant. Finally the low energies involved in astrophysical reactions limit the angular momenta ℓ_i to their lowest values. Examples are given in table 2.1, with the ^{3}He(α, γ)^{7}Be and ^{7}Be(p,γ)^{8}B reactions.

2.5 Transfer Cross Sections

In a transfer reaction, some nucleons are exchanged between the target and the projectile. A typical example in astrophysics is the ^{13}C(α,n)^{16}O reaction, where two protons and one neutron are stripped from the α particle to ^{13}C, to produce ^{16}O. Transfer processes arise from the nuclear interaction and the corresponding cross sections are usually much larger than the capture cross sections, arising from the electromagnetic interaction. For example, the ^{13}C(α,n)^{16}O cross section is larger by several order of magnitude than the ^{13}C(α, γ)^{17}O cross section.

Table 2.1 *Partial waves involved in the* $^3He(\alpha,\gamma)^7Be$ *and* $^7Be(p,\gamma)^8B$ *reactions (E1 multipole).*

	$J_f^{\pi_f}$	I	$J_i^{\pi_i}$	ℓ_i
$^3\text{He}(\alpha,\gamma)^7\text{Be}$	$3/2^-$	$1/2$	$1/2^+$	0
		$1/2$	$3/2^+$	2
		$1/2$	$5/2^+$	2
$^7\text{Be}(p,\gamma)^8\text{B}$	2^+	1	1^-	0
		1	2^-	2
		1	3^-	2,4
		2	1^-	2
		2	2^-	0,2,4
		2	3^-	2,4

To derive the transfer cross section, the wave function (2.2.11) must be generalized to reactions where the initial channel (i) is different from the final channel (f). If $\Omega = (\theta, \phi)$ is the relative direction of the nuclei in the final channel, the transfer cross section is given by

$$\frac{d\sigma_t}{d\Omega}(E, i \to f) = \frac{1}{(2I_1+1)(2I_2+1)} \sum_{\nu_1\nu_2,\nu_1'\nu_2'} |f_{i\nu_1\nu_2,f\nu_1'\nu_2'}(\theta)|^2, \quad (2.5.41)$$

where we have summed over the final orientation, and averaged over the initial orientations. A long but simple calculation provides

$$\frac{d\sigma_t}{d\Omega}(E, i \to f) = \frac{\pi}{k^2}\frac{1}{(2I_1+1)(2I_2+1)} \sum_j A_j(E)\, P_j(\cos\theta), \quad (2.5.42)$$

where $A_j(E)$ are given by

$$A_j(E) = \frac{1}{4\pi} \sum_{J\pi\ell LI} \sum_{J'\pi'\ell'L'I'} (-)^{I-I'} Z(j, J, J', \ell, L, I), \quad (2.5.43)$$

$$Z(j, J, J', \ell', L', I'), U_{i\ell I, f\ell' I'}^{J\pi}(E)\, U_{iLI, fL'I'}^{J'\pi'*}(E),$$

and are called anisotropy coefficients. Coefficients Z are defined as

$$Z(j, J, J', \ell, L, I) = [(2J+1)(2J'+1)(2\ell+1)$$

$$(2L+1)]^{\frac{1}{2}} <\ell\,0\,L\,0|j\,0> \left\{ \begin{array}{ccc} \ell & L & j \\ J' & J & I \end{array} \right\}, \quad (2.5.44)$$

and $U^{J\pi}$ represents the collision matrix generalized to multichannel systems. Again, definition (2.5.42) is model independent. The choice of the model only affects the collision matrix. In the following the R-matrix method will be used as an example. As for radiative capture, the important quantity in astrophysics is the integrated cross section

$$\sigma_t(E, i \to f) = \frac{\pi}{k^2} \sum_{J\pi} \frac{2J + 1}{(2I_1 + 1)(2I_2 + 1)} \sum_{\ell\ell'II'} |U^{J\pi}_{i\ell I, f\ell'I'}(E)|^2. \quad (2.5.45)$$

The discussion of subsect. 2.4 remains valid: in general a few terms are important in (2.5.45). Examples of angular momenta are given in table 2.2. Let us notice that, for the ^{7}Li(p,α)^{4}He reaction, the symmetry of the final channel limits the J^π values to $0^+, 2^+, 4^+$, etc., and consequently even angular momenta (in particular $\ell = 0$) are forbidden in the entrance channel.

2.6 Other Processes

2.6.1 Weak-Interaction Capture

For low-mass stars, nucleosynthesis is initiated by the p(p,$e^+\nu$)d reaction, which occurs through the weak interaction. Since the corresponding hamiltonian is much smaller than the nuclear and electromagnetic hamiltonians, the cross section is very small. Estimates in optimal experimental conditions [11] predict one event per 10^6 years ! Fortunately theoretical models are quite accurate [28]. The cross section is shown to be proportional to

$$\sigma_{pp}(E) \sim | < \Psi_d^{1^+}||\mathcal{M}_F + \lambda^2\mathcal{M}_{GT}||\Psi_{pp}(E) > |^2, \quad (2.6.46)$$

where $\Psi_d^{1^+}$ is the deuteron wave function, $\Psi_{pp}(E)$ is the scattering wave function and $\mathcal{M}_F$ and $\mathcal{M}_{GT}$ are the Fermi and Gamow-Teller operators, respectively. In (2.6.46), λ^2 is the ratio of axial-vector to vector coupling constants. A recent calculation [28] provides $S(0) \approx 3.9 \times 10^{-25}$ MeV-b, which is considerably lower than values obtained for capture or transfer reactions.

The ^{3}He(p,$e^+\nu$)^{4}He reaction plays a role in the high-energy part of the solar-neutrino spectrum [29], but its contribution to the nucleosynthesis is quite negligible. The cross section can be derived as previously, but the closed-shell structure of ^{4}He cancels out first-order terms. It is therefore sensitive to second-order components in the wave functions and in the

Table 2.2 *Partial waves involved in the* $^{13}C(\alpha,n)^{16}O$, $^{6}Li(p,\alpha)^{3}He$ *and* $^{7}Li(p,\alpha)^{4}He$ *reactions.*

	J^π	I	I'	ℓ	ℓ'
$^{13}C(\alpha,n)^{16}O$	$1/2^+$	$1/2$	$1/2$	1	0
	$1/2^-$	$1/2$	$1/2$	0	1
	$3/2^+$	$1/2$	$1/2$	1	2
	$3/2^-$	$1/2$	$1/2$	2	1
$^{6}Li(p,\alpha)^{3}He$	$1/2^+$	$1/2$	$1/2$	0	0
		$3/2$	$1/2$	2	0
	$1/2^-$	$1/2$	$1/2$	1	1
		$3/2$	$1/2$	1	1
	$3/2^+$	$1/2$	$1/2$	2	2
		$3/2$	$1/2$	$0,2$	2
	$3/2^-$	$1/2$	$1/2$	1	1
		$3/2$	$1/2$	$1,3$	1
$^{7}Li(p,\alpha)^{4}He$	0^+	1	0	1	0
	2^+	1	0	$1,3$	2
		2	0	$1,3$	2
	4^+	1	0	$3,5$	4
		2	0	$3,5$	4

weak-interaction hamiltonian. The reader is referred to refs [30, 31, 32, 33] for further information.

2.6.2   Neutron-Induced Reactions

In the s process, heavy elements are produced by (n,γ) reactions followed by β decay. The formalism developed above remains valid but some peculiarities appear. For $\eta = 0$, the Coulomb functions read [24]

$$
\begin{aligned}
F_\ell(x) &= x\, j_\ell(x) \\
G_\ell(x) &= -x\, y_\ell(x),
\end{aligned}
\tag{2.6.47}
$$

where $j_\ell(x)$ and $y_\ell(x)$ are the Bessel functions of first and second kind, respectively. For $\ell = 0$, the penetration and shift factors (2.3.26) become

$$P_0 = ka$$
$$S_0 = 0. \qquad (2.6.48)$$

and the low-energy cross section behaves as

$$\sigma_{n\gamma} \sim k^{2\ell_i - 1}. \qquad (2.6.49)$$

This energy dependence is typical of all neutron-induced reactions. It is quite different for $\ell_i = 0$, where the cross section increases as $1/k$, and for $\ell_i > 0$ where it tends to zero for low energies.

2.6.3 Three-Body Processes

Some astrophysical reactions involve three nuclei in the entrance channel [8]. A typical example is the triple-α process where three α particles fuse to form ^{12}C. This is a two-step process [34]: first, ^{8}Be is produced with a lifetime ($\sim 10^{-16}$) much larger than the mean time between two collisions ($\sim 10^{-19}$), which leads to an equilibrium between ^{8}Be and $\alpha + \alpha$. The second step is the ^{8}Be$(\alpha, \gamma)^{12}$C reaction, which proceeds through the well known 0_2^+ resonance located just above threshold.

Other three-body processes play a role in some stellar scenarios. For example the $\alpha(\alpha n, \gamma)^9$Be reaction is a source for the ^{9}Be nucleosynthesis [8]. Other processes such as $\alpha(nn,\gamma)^6$He or ^{15}O(pp,$\gamma)^{17}$Ne have been suggested [35] but remain poorly known.

2.6.4 Screening Effects

In stellar plasmas, atoms are usually completely ionized, and nuclear reactions involve bare nuclei. The situation is different in laboratories since target nuclei are partially or unionized. Consequently the role of the electron cloud cannot be neglected at low energies. Let us notice that screening effects, with a different origin, may also occur in stars. This process is poorly known [36], and much work remains to be done in this field.

The screening effect is usually evaluated through the screening potential U_e. The screening factor [37] is defined as

$$f(E) = \frac{\sigma_{exp}(E)}{\sigma_{th}(E)} = \frac{\sigma_{th}(E + U_e)}{\sigma_{th}(E)} \approx \exp(\pi\eta \frac{U_e}{E}), \qquad (2.6.50)$$

where $\sigma_{exp}(E)$ is the experimental cross section, affected by screening effects, and $\sigma_{th}(E)$ the theoretical cross section involving bare nuclei.

Screening effects have been observed for the first time in the ^{3}He(d,p)^{4}He reaction [38] and in reactions involving Li isotopes [39]. We give an example in fig.2.6.2 where the experimental ^{6}Li(p,α)^{3}He cross section is compared with a theoretical calculation involving nuclear effects only [40]. Obviously, theory can not account for the low-energy enhancement. A screening potential $U_e = 510$ eV provides a reasonable agreement with experiment.

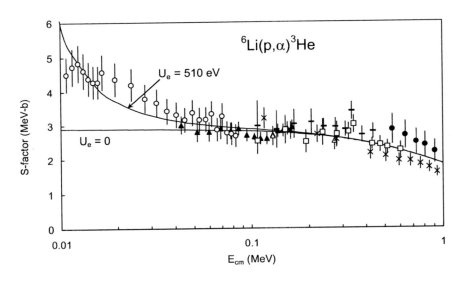

Figure 2.6.2: $^6Li(p,\alpha)^3He$ astrophysical factor with and without screening potential, compared with experimental data (taken from reference [40])).

Finally, let us make some remarks about the treatment of screening effects

- To derive U_e, it is necessary to know the cross section between bare nuclei. This cross section is usually extrapolated from a fit of higher energy data. This method is however sensitive to the cut-off energy and to the model adopted [40].

- Tremendous efforts to reach the Gamow peak energy are somewhat questionable. For example a recent measurement of the ^{3}He(^{3}He,2p)α cross section at solar energies [41] cannot be directly used for stellar models. Experimental data in this energy range must be corrected for electron screening by using previously obtained higher-energy data.

- The Trojan Horse Method seems to be a possible tool to avoid screening effects, and has been successfully applied to some reactions, such as ^{7}Li(p,α)^{4}He [42]. Of course this method is quite indirect, and depends on some assumptions on the transfer process.

2.7 Qualitative Discussion of Cross Sections

For light systems, all reactions present their own peculiarities, but it is possible to make some classification of reactions with similar properties. This is done in table 2.3 where there is a hierarchy between

1. transfer reactions (nuclear interaction)

2. capture reactions (electromagnetic interaction)

3. weak-capture reactions (weak interaction)

Table 2.3 *Classification of the main reactions involved in nuclear astrophysics.*

Process			Examples	$S(0)$ (MeV-b)
Nuclear	Non − resonant		^{6}Li(p,α)^{3}He	≈ 3
	Resonant	$\ell_R = \ell_{min}$	^{3}He(d, p)α	≈ 6
		$\ell_R > \ell_{min}$	^{11}B(p, α)^{8}Be	≈ 300
		multiresonance	^{22}Ne(α, n)^{25}Mg	$\approx 10^8$
	Subthreshold state		^{13}C(α, n)^{16}O	$\approx 10^7$
Electromagnetic	Non − resonant		^{6}Li(p,γ)^{7}Be	$\approx 10^{-4}$
	Resonant	$\ell_R = \ell_{min}$	^{12}C(p,γ)^{13}N	$\approx 10^{-3}$
		$\ell_R > \ell_{min}$	^{7}Be(p,γ)^{8}B	$\approx 2 \times 10^{-5}$
		multiresonance	^{22}Ne(α, γ)^{26}Mg	$\approx 2 \times 10^3$
	Subthreshold state		^{12}C(α, γ)^{16}O	≈ 0.5
Weak	Non-resonant		p(p,e$^+\nu$)d	$\approx 4 \times 10^{-25}$
			^{3}He(p,e$^+\nu$)^{4}He	$\approx 10^{-22}$

As shown in table 2.3, the cross sections follow this hierarchy. For example the ^{6}Li(p,α)^{3}He S factor is 10^4 larger than the ^{6}Li(p,γ)^{7}Be S factor. We also provide in table 2.3 an estimate of $S(0)$. Let us point out that comparison between S factors must be done carefully since they do not only depend on the cross sections, but also on the charges, through the Sommerfeld parameter.

For each process, we must make a difference between resonant and non-resonant reactions. A non-resonant reaction (also called "direct" reaction) does not have resonances at astrophysical energies. Typical examples are the ^{6}Li(p,α)^{3}He and ^{6}Li(p,γ)^{7}Be reactions where no resonance shows up below 1 MeV. For discussing resonant reactions it is useful to expand the cross section as

$$\sigma(E) = \sum_\ell \sigma_\ell(E), \qquad (2.7.51)$$

where $\sigma_\ell(E)$ is the cross section for partial wave ℓ. As shown by eqs. (2.4.41) and (2.5.45) there is no interference between different ℓ values in integrated cross sections. Let us assume an isolated resonance in partial wave ℓ_R. Two possibilities can be met according to whether ℓ_R is equal to ℓ_{min} (the lowest angular momentum allowed by the selection rules), or not.

- If $\ell_R \neq \ell_{min}$, eq. (2.7.51) gives

$$\sigma(E) \approx \sigma_{\ell_R}(E) + \sigma_{\ell_{min}}(E), \qquad (2.7.52)$$

and the resonance is superimposed on a non-resonant contribution. Examples are provided by the ^{7}Be(p,γ)^{8}B and ^{11}B(p,α)^{8}Be reactions which present $\ell = 1$ states at low energies.

- If $\ell_R = \ell_{min}$, we have

$$\sigma(E) \approx \sigma_{\ell_R}(E) \approx \sigma_{\ell_{min}}(E), \qquad (2.7.53)$$

and the distinction between resonant and non-resonant terms cannot be done rigorously. Non-resonant contributions arise from higher angular momenta which are strongly hindered by their large ℓ value and by their non-resonant nature. Examples are provided by the ^{12}C(p,γ)^{13}N and ^{15}N(p,α)^{12}C which present $\ell = 0$ low-energy resonances. In that case, the S factor is essentially determined by the resonance properties, even down to zero energy.

Some reactions are influenced by subthreshold states. This would correspond to a negative-energy resonance, which increases the S factor at low energies. A famous example is the ^{12}C(α, γ)^{16}O reaction which has 1^- and 2^+ states located just below threshold (-40 keV and -243 keV, respectively) [43].

The classification of table 2.3 is completed by weak-capture reactions which, as mentioned earlier, present minute cross sections.

2.8 Direct and Resonant Reactions

In the previous subsection, we showed that the treatment of resonances must be considered differently according to the ℓ-value of the resonance. Frequently a resonance with $\ell = \ell_{min}$ (usually $\ell_{min} = 0$) shows up in the energy range of astrophysical interest. Typical examples are $^{12}C(p,\gamma)^{13}N$ ($E_{cm} = 0.42$ MeV), $^{13}N(p,\gamma)^{14}O$ ($E_{cm} = 0.54$ MeV) or $^{14}N(p,\gamma)^{15}O$ ($E_{cm} = 0.26$ MeV). In this case, a confusion is often made in the literature concerning the resonant and non-resonant contributions. We briefly try here to explain the origin of this misunderstanding.

The differential capture cross section (2.4.37) can be rewritten by considering two partial waves ℓ_1 and ℓ_2 only, as

$$\frac{d\sigma_c}{d\Omega_\gamma}(E) \approx \sigma_{\ell_1}(E)W_{\ell_1}(\theta_\gamma) + \sigma_{\ell_2}(E)W_{\ell_2}(\theta_\gamma)$$

$$+2\sqrt{\sigma_{\ell_1}(E)\sigma_{\ell_2}(E)}\cos(\delta_{\ell_1} - \delta_{\ell_2} + \omega_{\ell_1} - \omega_{\ell_2})W_{\ell_1\ell_2}(\theta_\gamma) \quad (2.8.54)$$

where the angular functions have the following properties

$$\int W_{\ell_1}(\theta)\,d\Omega = \int W_{\ell_2}(\theta)\,d\Omega = 1,$$

$$\int W_{\ell_1\ell_2}(\theta)\,d\Omega = 0. \quad (2.8.55)$$

Equation (2.8.54) is equivalent to the cross section derived by Rolfs and Azuma (eq. (4) of Ref. [44]). Let us emphasize the main assumptions of eq. (2.8.54):

- It is valid for differential cross sections; when integrating over the photon angle θ_γ, the interference term vanishes.

- Explicitly it is assumed that $\ell_1 \neq \ell_2$; otherwise only the first term would remain. Equation (2.8.54) can be used if ℓ_1 contains a resonance ($\ell_1 = \ell_R$) and ℓ_2 does not ($\ell_2 = \ell_{NR}$).

In reactions presenting a low-energy resonance with $\ell_R = \ell_{min}$, eq (2.8.54) is often misused (see for example eq.(2) of ref. [45], eq.(8) of ref. [46], eq.(14) of ref. [47]). In this case the following assumptions are made:

- The resonant cross section (say $\sigma_{\ell_1}(E) = \sigma_{\ell_R}(E)$) is taken as a Breit-Wigner expression. This is of course an approximation which one tries to improve on. Then, a correction, called "direct process" is assumed to arise from $\sigma_{\ell_2}(E) = \sigma_{\ell_{NR}}(E)$, which is evaluated in the potential model, or with the hard-sphere approximation.

- The limitation to differential cross sections is disregarded, and the interference term is kept, whereas it cancels out when integrating over θ_γ.

Clearly, the problem takes its origin in the vocabulary used in this field. The definition "direct capture" is used in two different situations:

1. Contribution of partial waves which do not involve any resonance.

2. Correction to the Breit-Wigner approximation.

We use here the designation "direct capture" as defined by (1). Going beyond the Breit-Wigner approximation for the resonant contribution cannot be done by using the potential model since :

1. Either the potential does not reproduce the resonance energy, and is therefore meaningless.

2. Or the potential does contain the resonance, and a double counting is carried out.

More rigorous procedures would be either to use the potential model for the resonant partial waves, which ensures the correction to the Breit-Wigner approximation is treated consistently, or to apply methods such as the R-matrix theory which enables a simultaneous description of the resonant and background contributions.

In practice, the misunderstanding discussed here has a minor impact. For narrow resonances (typically $\Gamma < 100$ keV), the Breit-Wigner approximation provides a fairly good description of resonant processes. Then, corrections are always found to be small, or even negligible [45, 46, 47].

Chapter 3

The Potential Model

3.1 Introduction

Solving the Schrödinger equation associated with the hamiltonian (2.2.7) is in general very complex, and does not have an exact solution when the nucleon number is larger than three. The potential model is fairly simple to use, and has been applied to many reactions in low-energy nuclear physics [18, 19, 48, 49, 50]. The basic assumptions of the potential model are: (i) the nucleon-nucleon interaction leads to a nucleus-nucleus force, which depends on the relative coordinate only; (ii) the wave functions of the unified nucleus can be described by a cluster structure with $A_1 + A_2$ nucleons; (iii) the internal structure of the nuclei does not play any role.

Let us consider the nucleon coordinates r_i; the centers of mass of both nuclei read

$$
\begin{aligned}
R_1 &= \frac{1}{A_1} \sum_{i=1}^{A_1} r_i \\
R_2 &= \frac{1}{A_2} \sum_{i=A_1+1}^{A} r_i,
\end{aligned}
\tag{3.1.1}
$$

which provide the relative coordinate ρ and the c.m. coordinate R_{cm}

$$
\begin{aligned}
\rho &= R_1 - R_2 \\
R_{cm} &= \frac{1}{A}(A_1 R_1 + A_2 R_2).
\end{aligned}
\tag{3.1.2}
$$

Within each nucleus, we define the internal coordinates

$$
\begin{aligned}
\xi_1^i &= r_i - R_1 \quad \text{for } i \leq A_1 \\
\xi_2^i &= r_i - R_2 \quad \text{for } i > A_1.
\end{aligned}
\tag{3.1.3}
$$

Then the hamiltonian (2.2.7) is written as

$$H = H_1 + H_2 + T_{cm} + T_\rho + V(\rho), \qquad (3.1.4)$$

where H_1 and H_2 are the internal hamiltonians of nuclei 1 and 2 , T_{cm} is the c.m. energy and $V(\rho)$ is the nucleus-nucleus potential. Since each term of (3.1.4) acts in its own coordinate space, the total wave function factorizes out as

$$\Psi_{\ell I}^{JM\pi} = g_{\ell I}^{J\pi}(\rho) \; \varphi_{\ell I}^{JM\pi}(\Omega_\rho, \boldsymbol{\xi}_1^i, \boldsymbol{\xi}_2^j), \qquad (3.1.5)$$

where the channel function $\varphi_{\ell I}^{JM\pi}$ has been defined in (2.2.13), and where the c.m. motion has been removed. The radial function $g_{\ell J}^{J\pi}(\rho)$ is deduced from the equation

$$[T_\rho + V(\rho)] \, g_{\ell J}^{J\pi}(\rho) = E \, g_{\ell J}^{J\pi}(\rho), \qquad (3.1.6)$$

where E is the relative energy. Let us notice that the potential may depend on ℓ and J. In addition, the internal wave functions [see eq (2.2.9)] do not play any role in the system energy.

The Schrödinger equation (3.1.6) must be solved numerically for most potentials. Usually this equation is integrated by using the Numerov method [51, 52]. For bound states, the energy is obtained by requiring the wave function to be squared integrable. For scattering states, the numerical solution is fitted, at large distances, to a linear combination of Coulomb functions, which provides the phase shift. In single-channel calculations, it is obtained from the collision matrix as

$$U_\ell = \exp(2i\delta_\ell). \qquad (3.1.7)$$

The wave function is then normalized as in eq. (2.2.16).

3.2   Choice of the Potential

In nuclear physics, the nucleus-nucleus potential involves a Coulomb term V_C and a nuclear term V_N. Usually the Coulomb potential is parameterized as a point-sphere expression,

$$
\begin{aligned}
V_C(\rho) &= \frac{Z_1 Z_2 e^2}{2R_c} \left(3 - (\rho/R_c)^2\right) \text{ for } \rho \le R_c \\
&= \frac{Z_1 Z_2 e^2}{\rho} \text{ for } \rho > R_c,
\end{aligned} \qquad (3.2.8)
$$

where R_c is the sphere radius (typically the sum of the nuclear radii). According to the application, the choice of the nuclear contribution is guided by experimental constraints. In radiative-capture calculations it is crucial to reproduce the final-state energy. If phase shifts are available, they can be used to determine the initial potential. Frequently used nuclear terms are the Woods-Saxon potential

$$V_N(\rho) = \frac{V_0}{1 + \exp((\rho - \rho_0)/a)}, \tag{3.2.9}$$

or the Gaussian potential

$$V_N(\rho) = V_0 \exp(-(\rho/a)^2). \tag{3.2.10}$$

Additional terms, such as the spin-orbit or the tensor forces can be introduced without losing generality.

Besides experimental constraints, the nucleus-nucleus potential must follow requirements arising from microscopic arguments [18, 19]. The wave function (3.1.5) is a simplified form of a more general expression

$$\Psi_{\ell I}^{JM\pi} = \mathcal{A} \, g_{\ell I}^{J\pi}(\rho) \, \varphi_{\ell I}^{JM\pi}(\Omega_\rho, \xi_1^i, \xi_2^j), \tag{3.2.11}$$

where $\mathcal{A}$ is the antisymmetrization operator between all nucleons. This definition is used in microscopic models [19, 20] where all nucleons are taken into account. The antisymmetrization operator allows an exact treatment of the Pauli principle, but makes the calculation much more complicated than the potential model. It can be shown that, under some assumptions, there are non-vanishing radial functions which yield $\Psi_{\ell I}^{JM\pi} = 0$ after application of $\mathcal{A}$. These radial functions are called "forbidden states", and their number depends on the system and on the angular momentum. To illustrate the problem, let us consider the α+p system where the α particle is described in the shell model. Since the s-shell is filled by the α orbitals, the external proton can not occupy this s-shell state, which corresponds to a forbidden state. We refer the reader to refs [53, 18, 19] for more information.

The occurrence of forbidden states can be simulated by an adequate choice of the potential. According to Buck *et al.* [53], the potential must contain a number of bound states n_r, equal to the number of forbidden states. This prescription leads to deep potentials, since they involve additional (unphysical) bound states. The calculation of n_r is in general not obvious, except for nucleus-nucleon systems. Some examples are given in Table 3.1.

For the sake of completeness, let us mention that forbidden states can also be simulated by a singularity in the potential at $\rho = 0$. Both approaches are linked by a supersymmetry transformation [54], which will not be considered here.

Table 3.1 *Number of forbidden states for some systems.*

$\alpha + {}^3$He		^{7}Be+p		^{12}C+p	
ℓ	n_r	ℓ	n_r	ℓ	n_r
0	2	0	1	0	1
1,2	1	≥ 1	0	≥ 1	0
≥ 3	0				

3.3 Capture Cross Sections

In order to use the electromagnetic operators (2.4.32), we must explicit them in the coordinate system defined in subsect. 3.1. The c.m. motion is removed by using the Gartenhaus-Schwartz transformation [55], which defines a translation invariant form O' of an operator O by

$$O' = O(\mathbf{r_i} - \mathbf{R_{cm}}, \mathbf{p_i} - \mathbf{P_{cm}}/A), \qquad (3.3.12)$$

where $\mathbf{R_{cm}}$ and $\mathbf{P_{cm}}$ represent the c.m. coordinate and momentum, respectively. Within this transformation the $E1$, $E2$ and $M1$ operators are defined as

$$
\begin{aligned}
\mathcal{M}_{1\mu}^E &= e\left(Z_1\frac{A_2}{A} - Z_2\frac{A_1}{A}\right)\rho Y_1^\mu(\Omega_\rho) \\
\mathcal{M}_{2\mu}^E &= \mathcal{M}_{2\mu}^E(\boldsymbol{\xi}_1) + \mathcal{M}_{2\mu}^E(\boldsymbol{\xi}_2) + e\left(Z_1(\frac{A_2}{A})^2 + Z_2(\frac{A_1}{A})^2\right)\rho^2 Y_2^\mu(\Omega_\rho) \\
\mathcal{M}_{1\mu}^M &= \mathcal{M}_{1\mu}^M(\boldsymbol{\xi}_1) + \mathcal{M}_{1\mu}^M(\boldsymbol{\xi}_2) + \sqrt{\frac{3}{4\pi}}\,\mu_N\frac{Z_1A_2^2 + Z_2A_1^2}{A_1A_2A}\ell_\mu, \qquad (3.3.13)
\end{aligned}
$$

where internal operators appear for $E2$ and $M1$.

We give here matrix elements of (3.3.13) for zero-spin systems. A more general treatment is presented in Appendix A. If the internal spins are zero, matrix elements between wave functions (3.1.5) are obtained from

$$< \Psi^{J_f} || \mathcal{M}_\lambda^E || \Psi^{J_i} > \; = \; eF_E \int_0^\infty g^{J_f}(\rho) \rho^{\lambda+2} g^{J_i}(\rho) \, d\rho$$

$$< \Psi^{J_f} || \mathcal{M}_1^M || \Psi^{J_i} > \; = \; \mu_N F_M \int_0^\infty g^{J_f}(\rho) \rho^2 g^{J_i}(\rho) \, d\rho, \quad (3.3.14)$$

where the geometrical factors F_E and F_M are given by

$$F_E \; = \; \left[Z_1 (\frac{A_2}{A})^\lambda + Z_2 (\frac{-A_1}{A})^\lambda \right] \left[\frac{(2\lambda+1)(2J_i+1)}{4\pi(2J_f+1)} \right]^{\frac{1}{2}} < J_i \, 0 \, \lambda \, 0 | J_f \, 0 >$$

$$F_M \; = \; \frac{Z_1 A_2^2 + Z_2 A_1^2}{A_1 A_2 A} \left[\frac{3 J_f (J_f+1)}{4\pi} \right]^{\frac{1}{2}} \delta_{J_i J_f}. \quad (3.3.15)$$

When the internal spins are different from zero, eqs. (3.3.14) involve additional terms related to the internal moments of nuclei 1 and 2. In any case, the matrix elements are obtained from one-dimensional integrals. With the matrix elements, capture cross sections can be determined with eq. (2.4.37) or (2.4.41). Spectroscopic properties, such as r.m.s. radii, quadrupole moments or electromagnetic transition probabilities can be also deduced in the potential model, using equations similar to (3.3.14), with initial and final bound-state wave functions.

In numerical applications, the natural asymptotic normalization of the scattering state is

$$g_{\ell I}^{J\pi,as}(\rho) \underset{\rho \to \infty}{\to} (\cos \delta^{J\ell I} F_\ell(k\rho) + \sin \delta^{J\ell I} G_\ell(k\rho))/\rho, \quad (3.3.16)$$

which, up to a phase and a normalization factor, is quite equivalent to (2.2.16). In these conditions the electric part of the capture cross section is given by

$$\sigma_{J_f,\lambda}(E) = 8\pi \frac{e^2}{\hbar v k^2} \left[Z_1 \left(\frac{A_2}{A}\right)^\lambda + Z_2 \left(\frac{-A_1}{A}\right)^\lambda \right]^2 \sum_{J_i,I,\ell_i} k_\gamma^{2\lambda+1} \frac{(\lambda+1)(2\lambda+1)}{\lambda[(2\lambda+1)!!]^2} \quad (3.3.17)$$

$$\times \frac{(2\ell_f+1)(2J_f+1)(2J_i+1)}{(2I_1+1)(2I_2+1)} < \ell_f 0 \lambda 0 | \ell_i 0 >^2$$

$$\left\{ \begin{matrix} J_i & \ell_i & I \\ \ell_f & J_f & \lambda \end{matrix} \right\}^2 \left(\int_0^\infty g_{\ell_i I}^{J_i \pi_i}(\rho) \rho^{\lambda+2} g_{\ell_f I}^{J_f \pi_f}(\rho) \, d\rho \right)^2.$$

3.4   Applications

3.4.1   The ^{3}He$(\alpha, \gamma)^7$Be, ^{7}Be$(p,\gamma)^8$B and ^{12}C$(p,\gamma)^{13}$N Reactions

We present here some applications of the potential model to radiative-capture reactions. Three typical examples, providing an overview of most situations, are considered:

- The non-resonant reactions ^{3}He$(\alpha, \gamma)^7$Be and ^{7}Be$(p,\gamma)^8$B.

- The ^{12}C$(p,\gamma)^{13}$N reaction which presents a low-energy resonance with $\ell = 0$.

We use a Gaussian potential (3.2.10) for the nuclear interaction, with a point-sphere approximation (3.2.8) for the Coulomb term. The parameters are given in table 3.2; for the ^{3}He$(\alpha, \gamma)^7$Be and ^{7}Be$(p,\gamma)^8$B reactions they resemble those of refs [50] and [56], respectively. The final potential is fitted to reproduce the binding energy of the final state. For the ^{12}C$(p,\gamma)^{13}$N reaction, the initial potential is constrained by the energy and width of the $1/2^+$ ($E_{c.m.} = 0.42$ MeV, $\Gamma_p = 32$ keV) state. The potentials are indicative only; they are not fitted to any cross section data and should not be considered as "optimal potentials".

Astrophysical S-factors are displayed in fig.3.4.1, and compared with available data. For the ^{3}He$(\alpha, \gamma)^7$Be reaction, two contributions, corresponding to the $3/2^-$ and $1/2^-$ bound states of ^{7}Be, must be considered. The ground-state contribution is favored by the E_γ^3 term showing up in the $E1$ cross section. Below 0.5 MeV, the s wave is dominant, but the d wave cannot be neglected to reproduce the energy dependence from 0 to 3 MeV.

The ^{7}Be$(p,\gamma)^8$B cross section presents a 1^+ resonance at $E_{c.m.} = 0.63$ MeV. This resonance is a p wave and decays to the ground state by $M1$ transition. Off resonance, its contribution is negligible and is not taken into account here. In order to evaluate the sensitivity of the S factor with respect to the potential, different ranges a have been used, with a readjustment of V_0 to reproduce the ^{8}B binding energy. The main effect is a scaling factor, as we will show in the next subsections.

The ^{12}C$(p,\gamma)^{13}$N S-factor is essentially determined by the properties of the $1/2^+$ resonance at 0.42 MeV. In contrast to ^{7}Be$(p,\gamma)^8$B, this resonance is an s wave and its contribution extends over a wide energy range. With the adopted parameters, the potential model overestimates the data by a factor of two. This effect is well known and arises from

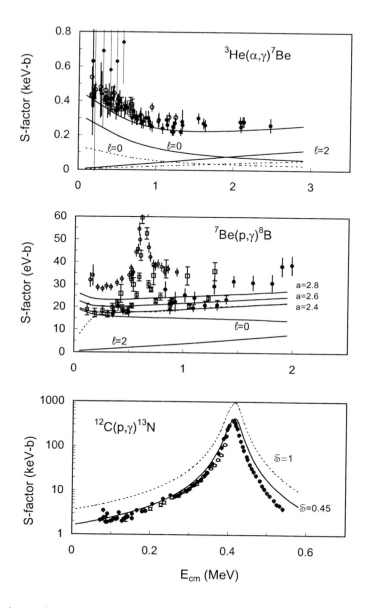

Figure 3.4.1: *Astrophysical S factors in the potential model.* $^3He(\alpha,\gamma)^7Be$: *solid lines correspond to the 3/2⁻ ground state, and dotted lines correspond to the 1/2⁻ excited state.* $^7Be(p,\gamma)^8B$: *the calculations are done for different ranges of the Gaussian potential; dotted lines are obtained by using 50 fm as an upper limit for the radial integral. The symbols follow the notations of Ref. [9].*

Table 3.2 *Parameters of Gaussian potentials.*

	$^3\mathrm{He}(\alpha,\gamma)^7\mathrm{Be}$	$^7\mathrm{Be}(\mathrm{p},\gamma)^8\mathrm{B}$	$^{12}\mathrm{C}(\mathrm{p},\gamma)^{13}\mathrm{N}$
R_c (fm)	3.25	2.4	2.7
Final state			
E_f (MeV)	$-1.59, -1.16$	-0.137	-1.94
ℓ_f	1	1	1
J_f	$3/2^-, 1/2^-$	2^+	$1/2^-$
a (fm)	2.48	2.8	2.7
V_0 (MeV)	$-86.6, -84.8$	-44.81	-56.4
Initial state			
ℓ_i	0, 2	0, 2	0
J_i	$1/2^+, 3/2^+, 5/2^+$	2^-	$1/2^+$
a (fm)	2.48	2.8	2.7
V_0 (MeV)	-67.7	-44.81	-70.5

the basic assumption of the potential model: a pure $^{12}\mathrm{C}+\mathrm{p}$ structure for the $^{13}\mathrm{N}$ ground state. A more realistic wave function would involve other components such as $^{12}\mathrm{C}^*+\mathrm{p}$ for instance, which would reduce the $^{12}\mathrm{C}+\mathrm{p}$ amplitude. This effect is simulated by a spectroscopic factor $\mathcal{S}$ which scales the $^{13}\mathrm{N}$ wave function by $\sqrt{\mathcal{S}}$ and therefore the cross section by $\mathcal{S}$. Figure 3.4.1 shows that using $\mathcal{S} = 0.45$ provides a good agreement with the data. This value is consistent with the spectroscopic factor derived by Rolfs and Azuma [44] ($\mathcal{S} = 0.49 \pm 0.15$).

The energy dependence of the cross sections is given by the scattering wave functions which, in turn, essentially depend on the phase shifts. In fig. 3.4.2 we show the phase shift (3.1.7) for $\ell = 0$. The $^{12}\mathrm{C}+\mathrm{p}$ phase shift presents a bump at 0.42 MeV, typical of narrow resonances. The non-resonant $^7\mathrm{Be}+\mathrm{p}$ and $^3\mathrm{He}+\alpha$ phase shifts have a smooth energy dependence.

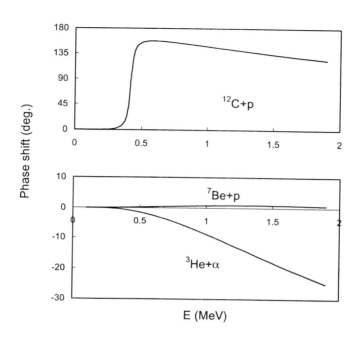

Figure 3.4.2: *Phase shifts for the* $^{12}C+p$, $^{7}Be+p$ *and* $^{3}He+\alpha$
systems $(\ell = 0)$.

3.4.2   Analysis of the Cross Sections

As discussed in sect 3.3, the cross sections are determined from integrals
involving the initial and final wave functions. Let us define

$$I(\rho) = g^{J_f}(\rho)\rho^{\lambda+2}g^{J_i}(\rho), \qquad (3.4.18)$$

whose integral provides the electric component of the cross section. In
Fig. 3.4.3, we present this integrand for typical energies. For the
$^{12}C(p,\gamma)^{13}N$ reaction, the maximum of $I(\rho)$ is located near ρ_{max} of 4 fm,
whereas it is near 10 fm for $^{3}He(\alpha,\gamma)^{7}Be$. At low energy the initial function $g^{J_i}(\rho)$ decreases rapidly in the nuclear region; conversely, the final
function $g^{J_f}(\rho)$ is maximal in this region, and exponentially decreases as

$$g^{J_f}(\rho) = C_f\, W_{-\eta,\ell_f+\frac{1}{2}}(2k\rho)/\rho \sim C_f\, \exp(-k\rho)/\rho^{\eta+1} \qquad (3.4.19)$$

as discussed in sect. 2.2.

The decrease is therefore faster for large k values, and hence for large
binding energies. For very low binding energies, such as ^{8}B $(-137$ keV),

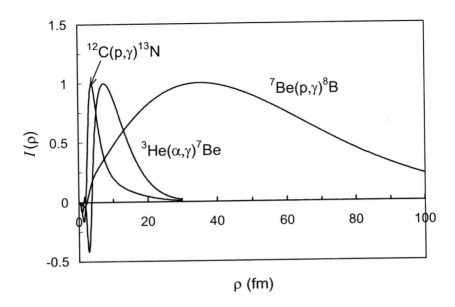

Figure 3.4.3: *Integrand (3.4.18) at 0.02 MeV for $^7Be(p,\gamma)^8B$, and at 0.1 MeV for $^3He(\alpha,\gamma)^7Be$ and $^{12}C(p,\gamma)^{13}N$. The normalization is arbitrary.*

we have $\rho_{max} \approx 40$ fm and integrand (3.4.18) is non negligible up to 150 fm. Accordingly, integrals (3.3.14) must be performed up to large ρ values. For $^7Be(p,\gamma)^8B$, results presented in Fig. 3.4.1 have been obtained by integrating up to 200 fm; dashed lines correspond to 50 fm as an upper limit. It is obvious that the energy dependence below 0.2 MeV is meaningless with the latter value. This problem is discussed in more detail in ref.[19].

3.4.3   The Extranuclear Capture Model

Figure 3.4.3 shows that, for low binding energies, the main contribution to integral (3.3.14) arises from large distances. This result is the basis of the extranuclear capture model [57], which does not require any potential. The wave functions are given by their asymptotic limits. The phase shift is assumed to be zero, or to be defined in the hard-sphere approximation. According to these assumptions, the S factor reads

$$S_f(E) \approx |C_f|^2 \, \tilde{S}_f(E), \tag{3.4.20}$$

where $\tilde{S}_f(E)$ only depends on basic properties of the system, such as charges, masses, binding energies, and angular momenta; it is model independent. The only quantity to be known is the amplitude C_f or the asymptotic normalization constant (ANC) [58]. The importance of the ^{7}Be(p,γ)^{8}B reaction lead several groups to measure C_f. These indirect methods aim at transferring one proton to ^{7}Be with reactions such as ^{7}Be(d,n)^{8}B or ^{7}Be(^{3}He,d)^{8}B for example [59]. Notice however that the determination of C_f requires poorly known inputs such as nucleus-nucleus potentials, which reduces the accuracy of the method [60].

3.5 Limitations of the Potential Model

The main advantage of the potential model is its simplicity. However it assumes from the very beginning that the final bound state presents the two-body structure of the entrance channel. This is also true for resonances, which must be described by the adopted nucleus-nucleus structure. This hypothesis is not always valid. In the ^{16}O(α, γ)^{20}Ne reaction for example, the 0_1^+ ground state and the 0_4^+ broad resonance are well described by an $\alpha+^{16}$O structure, but the 0_2^+ and 0_3^+ resonances would require other configurations, such as $\alpha+^{16}$O* or p+^{19}F. This problem is more and more frequent as the level density increases. Another well known example is the ^{15}O(α, γ)^{19}Ne reaction where most of the ^{19}Ne low-lying states can be accurately reproduced by an $\alpha+^{15}$O structure, but where the resonance important for astrophysics (3/2$^+$ at $E_{c.m.} = 0.50$ MeV) most likely presents an other structure.

Chapter 4

The R-Matrix Method

4.1 Introduction

In astrophysics, the main goal of the R-matrix method [15, 61] is to parameterize some experimentally known quantities, such as cross sections or phase shifts, with a small number of parameters, which are then used to extrapolate the cross section down to low energies. The R-matrix approach involves "poles" which correspond to bound states or resonances; R-matrix parameters are related to experimental values, but not equal to them. The link between experimental parameters ("observed" parameters) and R-matrix parameters ("calculated" or "formal" parameters) is one of the main difficulties of the method. We will discuss this link in the following. The R-matrix method assumes that the space is divided into two regions:

- the internal region, where the nuclear force takes place, and where the physics of the problem is derived from the properties of the poles;

- the external region, where only the Coulomb force remains.

The radius of the internal region is called the R-matrix radius and is denoted as a. Up to the numerical accuracy, the final results must be insensitive to its choice. Many applications have been developed within the R-matrix theory, not only in astrophysics [43, 62, 63] but also to describe other nuclear properties such as β decay [64] or Coulomb displacement energies [65]. Here, we aim at presenting an outline of the R-matrix method, by emphasizing applications to nuclear astrophysics. We mainly assume single-channel calculations involving zero-spin nuclei.

Generalization is straightforward but makes the notation more complicated. Further details can be found in the work of Lane and Thomas,
which is the basic reference dealing with the R-matrix method [15].

The R-matrix method can also be applied for other purposes. In most
variational calculations, the basis wave functions are adapted to a limited
region, but can not describe scattering states. The R-matrix is then a
good tool to derive scattering properties. The "formal" parameters are
not fitted to experiment, but are calculated from the basis wave functions.
Applications in nuclear and atomic physics can be found in Refs [66] and
[67]. We will not discuss this approach here.

4.2 Elastic Phase Shifts

4.2.1 General Formalism

As mentioned before, we limit the presentation to single-channel zero-spin
systems. The wave functions are therefore characterized by the relative
angular momentum ℓ. The main purpose of the R-matrix method is to
derive an approximate solution of the Schrödinger equation

$$(H - E)\,\Psi^{\ell m} = 0, \tag{4.2.1}$$

where $\Psi^{\ell m}$ is the two-body wave function. Let us consider a set of N
basis functions

$$\varphi_i^{\ell m} = \frac{u_i^\ell(\rho)}{\rho}\,Y_\ell^m(\Omega_\rho), \tag{4.2.2}$$

which are solutions of eq.(4.2.1) over the internal region

$$\left(H - E_i^\ell\right)\varphi_i^{\ell m} = 0, \tag{4.2.3}$$

where E_i^ℓ are the eigenvalues. These wave functions are supposed to be
orthonormal over the internal region

$$\int_0^a u_i^\ell(\rho)u_j^\ell(\rho)\,d\rho = \delta_{ij}, \tag{4.2.4}$$

and to have zero derivative at the surface

$$\left(\frac{du_i^\ell(\rho)}{d\rho}\right)_{\rho=a} = 0. \tag{4.2.5}$$

The total wave function $\Psi^{\ell m}$ is then factored as

$$\Psi^{\ell m} = \frac{g^{\ell}(\rho)}{\rho} Y_{\ell}^{m}(\Omega_{\rho}), \tag{4.2.6}$$

with

$$
\begin{aligned}
g^{\ell}(\rho) &= \sum_{i=1}^{N} A_i^{\ell} \, u_i^{\ell}(\rho) \text{ for } \rho \leq a \\
&= i^{\ell+1}(\pi(2\ell+1)/v)^{1/2} \left[I_{\ell}(k\rho) - U^{\ell} O_{\ell}(k\rho) \right] / k \text{ for } \rho > a, \tag{4.2.7}
\end{aligned}
$$

where the normalization is chosen according to (2.2.16). The unknown parameters are the expansion coefficients A_i^{ℓ} and the collision matrix U^{ℓ} (in single-channel calculations this matrix reduces to a number). Multiplying (4.2.1) by $\varphi_i^{\ell m*}$ and (4.2.3) by $\Psi^{\ell m*}$, and subtracting both equations provides

$$A_i = \frac{\hbar^2}{2\mu m_N} \frac{u_i(a) g'(a)}{E_i - E}, \tag{4.2.8}$$

where we have dropped the index ℓ. Using the continuity of the wave function (4.2.7) at the surface, we have

$$g(\rho) = G(\rho, a) a g'(a), \tag{4.2.9}$$

where the Green's function is defined as

$$G(\rho, a) = \frac{\hbar^2}{2\mu m_N a} \sum_i \frac{u_i(a) u_i(\rho)}{E_i - E}. \tag{4.2.10}$$

Then, we derive the R-matrix

$$R = G(a, a) = \sum_i \frac{\tilde{\gamma}_i^2}{E_i - E} = \frac{g(a)}{a g'(a)}, \tag{4.2.11}$$

where the formal reduced width $\tilde{\gamma}_i^2$ is given by

$$\tilde{\gamma}_i = \left(\frac{\hbar^2}{2\mu m_N a} \right)^{1/2} u_i^{\ell}(a). \tag{4.2.12}$$

We denote formal quantities by the notation $\sim$. The reduced width is directly related to the wave function at the R-matrix radius. Of course, it depends on this radius as the R matrix does; this radius dependence is canceled by the Coulomb functions which makes the collision matrix almost independent of a. Let us point out that definition (4.2.12) holds for both negative and positive energy states. A large reduced width means that the corresponding state presents a strong deformation, whereas a small reduced width is typical of spherical states. In general, one uses the dimensionless reduced width

$$\theta_i^2 = \tilde{\gamma}_i^2 / \gamma_W^2, \tag{4.2.13}$$

where $\gamma_W^2 = 3\hbar^2 / 2\mu m_N a^2$ is the Wigner limit.

Equation (4.2.11) shows that the R-matrix is the inverse of the logarithmic derivative of the wave function at the surface. Using (4.2.7) provides the collision matrix

$$U = \frac{I(ka)}{O(ka)} \frac{1 - L^\star R}{1 - LR}, \tag{4.2.14}$$

where we have used (2.3.25). Notice that, from here, we drop index ℓ to simplify the notation. As shown in appendix B, eq. (4.2.14) is equivalent to

$$U = \frac{I(ka)}{O(ka)} \left(1 + i \sum_{ij} (B^{-1})_{ij} \sqrt{\tilde{\Gamma}_i \tilde{\Gamma}_j} \right), \tag{4.2.15}$$

where matrix B is defined by

$$B_{ij} = (E_i - E)\delta_{ij} - L\tilde{\gamma}_i \tilde{\gamma}_j, \tag{4.2.16}$$

and where we introduce the total width

$$\tilde{\Gamma}_i = 2\tilde{\gamma}_i^2 P(E_i). \tag{4.2.17}$$

The collision matrix is written as

$$U = \exp(2i\delta) = \exp(2i(\omega + \delta_{HS} + \delta_R)), \tag{4.2.18}$$

where δ_{HS} is the hard-sphere phase shift which is obtained with $R = 0$, and therefore with $\tilde{\gamma}_i^2 = 0$. It corresponds to wave functions vanishing at the surface, which justifies the designation "hard sphere". It is obtained from

$$\exp(2i(\omega + \delta_{HS})) = \frac{I(ka)}{O(ka)}$$

$$\delta_{HS} = -\arctan \frac{F(ka)}{G(ka)}. \tag{4.2.19}$$

The R-matrix phase shift is deduced from (4.2.14)

$$\delta_{\text{R}} = \arctan \frac{PR}{1 - SR}, \tag{4.2.20}$$

where the penetration and shift factors have been defined in (2.3.26). In general the phase shift is referred to as the nuclear phase shift

$$\delta_{\text{N}} = \delta_{\text{HS}} + \delta_{\text{R}}. \tag{4.2.21}$$

Let us mention that this development can be made with more general boundary conditions in (4.2.5). Assuming $u'(a) = B$ is equivalent to the substitution of S in (4.2.20) by $S - B$. This approach is useful when a single pole is involved, but also simplifies the method in a general N-pole calculation. Details can be found in ref. [15].

4.2.2 Link between "Observed" and "Calculated" Parameters

As mentioned before, the pole energies E_i and reduced widths $\tilde{\gamma}_i^2$ are associated with the poles of the R-matrix, and therefore depend on conditions of the calculation such as the radius a. The resonance energy E_i^{r}, or the "observed" energy, is defined as the energy where the R-matrix phase shift is $\delta_R = \pi/2$. According to (4.2.20), E_i^{r} is therefore a solution of the equation

$$S(E_i^{\text{r}})R(E_i^{\text{r}}) = 1. \tag{4.2.22}$$

On the other hand, the "observed" width enters the Breit-Wigner parameterization near the resonance energy

$$\delta_{\text{R}}(E) \approx \arctan \frac{\Gamma_i(E)}{2(E_i^{\text{r}} - E)}, \tag{4.2.23}$$

which gives, by using (4.2.20)

$$\Gamma_i(E) = 2P(E) \frac{R(E_i^{\text{r}})}{[S(E)R(E)]'_{E=E_i^{\text{r}}}} = 2P(E)\,\gamma_i^2, \tag{4.2.24}$$

and defines γ_i^2 as the *"observed"* reduced width of the resonance. We also have

$$\Gamma_i(E) = \Gamma_i \frac{P(E)}{P(E_i^{\text{r}})}, \tag{4.2.25}$$

where Γ_i is the width calculated at the resonance energy.

If the pole number N is larger than unity, the link between observed and calculated parameters is not analytical and requires numerical calculations [68]. We illustrate here a simple but frequent situation where $N = 1$. The phase shift (4.2.20) is

$$\delta_R(E) = \arctan \frac{\tilde{\Gamma}_1(E)}{2(E_1 - E - \tilde{\gamma}_1^2 S(E))}, \qquad (4.2.26)$$

which is equivalent to (4.2.23) if we set

$$E_1^r = E_1 - \tilde{\gamma}_1^2 S(E_1^r)$$
$$\gamma_1^2 = \tilde{\gamma}_1^2 / \left(1 + \tilde{\gamma}_1^2 S'(E_1^r)\right), \qquad (4.2.27)$$

where $S'(E) = dS/dE$. These formulas provide a simple link between calculated and observed values. To derive (4.2.27) we have used the Thomas approximation where the shift factor is linearized near E_1^r:

$$S(E) \approx S(E_1^r) + (E - E_1^r)S'(E_1^r). \qquad (4.2.28)$$

This approximation is in general quite accurate (see Fig. (2.1.1)). The term $\gamma_1^2 S'(E_1^r)$ is called the shift factor; it is proportional to the reduced width and is therefore large for strongly deformed states.

Finally, let us make two important comments:

1. The difference between observed and calculated parameters arises from different definitions of the Breit-Wigner approximation. In definition (4.2.26), the shift factor is explicitly taken into account, whereas definition (4.2.23) does not involve this term. Both definitions are equivalent near the resonance energy provided the parameters are defined consistently.

2. We have assumed resonant reactions, but the R-matrix theory can be applied to non-resonant reactions as well. In this case, high-energy poles are gathered in the R-matrix expansion, and provide a background contribution. Definitions (4.2.14) and (4.2.20) are still applicable with a constant R matrix

$$R(E) = R_0. \qquad (4.2.29)$$

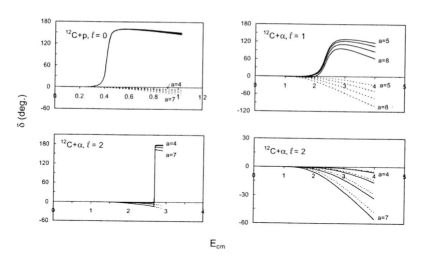

Figure 4.2.1: *R-matrix phase shifts for resonant systems, calculated with parameters of Table 4.1. Hard-sphere phase shifts are plotted as dotted lines.*

4.2.3 Examples

We show here some applications to resonant and non-resonant systems. Resonant calculations are illustrated by four typical examples:

1. The ^{12}C+p system which presents a narrow resonance $1/2^{+}(\ell = 0)$ at $E^{r} = 0.42$ MeV with a width of 32 keV. The small width arises from the low energy of the state; the dimensionless reduced width is large and is typical of cluster states.

2. The ^{12}C+α system with the 1^{-} resonance ($E^{r} = 2.42$ MeV, $\Gamma = 0.42$ MeV) which is typical of broad resonances.

3. The 2_{2}^{+} resonance at $E^{r} = 2.683$ MeV of the ^{12}C+α system ($\Gamma = 0.625$ keV) which presents a very small reduced width. This state is characterized by a dominant ^{12}C$^{*} + \alpha$ structure [69].

4. The 2_{1}^{+} bound state ($E^{r} = -0.24$ MeV) of the ^{12}C+α system. We have taken a typical value $\gamma^{2} = 0.2$ MeV.

In table 4.1, we present the R-matrix parameters for different radii. Figure 4.1 shows the corresponding phase shifts, and the hard-sphere phase

Table 4.1 *R-matrix parameters of resonant systems.*

	$a = 4$ fm	$a = 5$ fm	$a = 6$ fm	$a = 7$ fm
^{12}C+p ($E^r = 0.42$ MeV, $\Gamma = 32$ keV, $J = 1/2^+, \ell = 0$)				
γ^2 (MeV)	1.09	0.59	0.35	0.23
E_0 (MeV)	-2.15	-0.61	-0.11	0.11
$\tilde{\gamma}^2$ (MeV)	3.09	1.16	0.57	0.32
θ^2 (%)	25.8	22.0	18.8	10.5
^{12}C+α ($E^r = 2.42$ MeV, $\Gamma = 0.42$ MeV, $J = 1^-, \ell = 1$)				
γ^2 (MeV)		0.57	0.28	0.16
E_0 (MeV)		0.49	1.92	2.22
$\tilde{\gamma}^2$ (MeV)		1.17	0.37	0.19
θ^2 (%)		69.2	48.1	38.8
^{12}C+α ($E^r = 2.683$ MeV, $\Gamma = 0.625$ keV, $J = 2^+, \ell = 2$)				
γ^2 (keV)	4.56	1.28	0.517	0.275
E_0 (MeV)	2.672	2.680	2.682	2.683
$\tilde{\gamma}^2$ (keV)	4.56	1.28	0.511	0.275
θ^2 (%)	0.35	0.15	0.09	0.06
^{12}C+α ($E^r = -0.24$ MeV, $\gamma^2 = 0.2$ MeV, $J = 2^+, \ell = 2$)				
E_0 (MeV)	-1.05	-1.14	-1.25	-1.36
$\tilde{\gamma}^2$ (MeV)	0.21	0.22	0.23	0.24
θ^2 (%)	15.4	24.2	34.7	47.3

shifts. The ^{12}C+p resonance presents a large reduced width and, therefore, a large shift. For small a values, the pole energy E_0 is negative although the observed value E^r is positive. In spite of quite different R-matrix parameters, the phase shifts corresponding to different radii cannot be distinguished on the scale of the figure.

A similar situation occurs for the 1^- broad resonance of the ^{12}C+α system. The reduced width is quite large and typical of cluster states. Since the energy shift is significant, special attention must be paid to the validity of the Thomas approximation (linearization of the shift factor, see sect. 2.3). In the present case, this approximation is not valid below $a \approx 5$ fm. The calculated values E_0 and $\tilde{\gamma}^2$ should be determined from the general equation (4.2.22) with the exact definition of the shift factor. The situation is simpler for the 2_2^+ resonance whose reduced width is very small (less than 1% of the Wigner limit). In this case the shift is negligible and the observed values are very close to the formal values. For the 2_1^+ bound state, we have chosen $\gamma^2 = 0.2$ MeV for all a values, since the total width is not defined at negative energies. Of course, taking a common value means that the conditions of the calculation are not identical for each radius (the deformation is increasing with a). Accordingly the phase shifts are sensitive to the R-matrix radius.

In Fig. 4.2, we apply the R-matrix formalism to the $\alpha+^3$He and ^{7}Be+p non-resonant systems ($\ell = 0$). The "reference" phase shifts have been generated by the potential model (see sect. 3) since no experimental values are available for ^{7}Be+p. In each case the non-resonant behaviour has been simulated by a high-energy pole. For the $\alpha+^3$He system, the phase shift is well reproduced by the hard-sphere approximation with $a = 3$ fm. Increasing this radius requires a background term. With $E^r = 5$ MeV and $\Gamma = 3.5$ MeV, the R-matrix method can fit the phase shift for a radius $a = 4$ fm. The situation is different for the ^{7}Be+p system. Since the reference phase shift is positive, it can not be adjusted by a hard-sphere term only. Again, the sets ($E^r = 8.5$ MeV, $\Gamma = 15$ MeV) for $a = 2$ fm and ($E^r = 7$ MeV, $\Gamma = 15$ MeV) for $a = 3$ fm provide a good fit up to 2 MeV.

4.3   Transfer Cross Sections

4.3.1   General Formalism

The R-matrix theory developed in previous subsections only concerns single-channel systems or, in other words, one-dimension R matrices. To

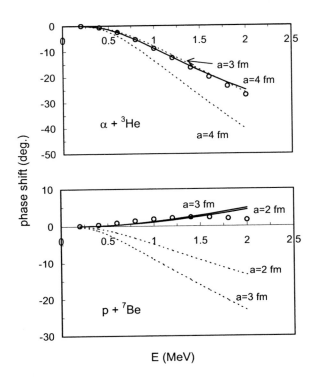

Figure 4.2.2: *Elastic phase shifts of the $\alpha+^3He$ and ^7Be+p ($\ell = 0$) systems fitted by the R-matrix method with an high-energy pole (see text). Dashed lines correspond to the hard sphere phase shifts δ_{HS}.*

deal with transfer reactions, the formalism must be extended to multichannel systems. We present here the main results, and refer the reader to refs [15, 40, 70] for detail. Extension of the R-matrix (4.2.11) to multichannel problems yields

$$R_{\alpha\beta}(E) = \sum_i \frac{\tilde{\gamma}_{i,\alpha}\tilde{\gamma}_{i,\beta}}{E_i - E}, \qquad (4.3.30)$$

where $\tilde{\gamma}_{i,\alpha}^2$ is the reduced width of pole i in channel α. If we consider the $^6Li(p,\alpha)^3He$ reaction, labels α and β take the values 1 and 2 for the ^6Li+p and $\alpha+^3He$ channels, respectively, and R_{12} refers to the transfers between these channels. It can be shown [15] that the collision matrix (4.2.14) is generalized as

$$U(E) = (Z^\star(E))^{-1} Z(E), \qquad (4.3.31)$$

where matrix $\mathbf{Z}$ is defined by

$$Z_{\alpha\beta}(E) = I_\alpha(E)\,\delta_{\alpha\beta} - a\,\sqrt{k_\alpha k_\beta}\,R_{\alpha\beta}(E)\,I'_\beta(E), \qquad (4.3.32)$$

and where indices corresponding to spins and angular momenta have been dropped for the sake of clarity. If the pole number is larger than unity, the link between observed and calculated values is rather complicated. We limit ourselves to $N = 1$, and to two-channel systems (α and β are equal to 1 or 2). Using (4.3.31) and (4.3.32) provides

$$U_{11} = \frac{I_1}{O_1}\frac{1 - R_{11}L_1^\star - R_{22}L_2}{1 - R_{11}L_1 - R_{22}L_2}, \qquad (4.3.33)$$

$$U_{22} = \frac{I_2}{O_2}\frac{1 - R_{11}L_1 - R_{22}L_2^\star}{1 - R_{11}L_1 - R_{22}L_2},$$

$$U_{12} = U_{21} = \frac{2ia\sqrt{k_1 k_2}\sqrt{R_{11}R_{22}}}{O_1 O_2\,(1 - R_{11}L_1 - R_{22}L_2)},$$

where L_1 and L_2 are the constants (2.3.25) in channels 1 and 2. In transfer reactions, the Breit-Wigner approximation of the cross section is given by

$$\sigma_t(E) \approx \frac{\pi}{k_1^2}\frac{2J+1}{(2I_1+1)(2I_2+1)}\frac{\Gamma_1(E)\Gamma_2(E)}{(E - E_1^r)^2 + \Gamma(E)^2/4}, \qquad (4.3.34)$$

where J is the spin of the resonance, Γ_1 and Γ_2 are the partial widths ($\Gamma = \Gamma_1 + \Gamma_2$), and I_1, I_2 are the spins of the colliding nuclei in the entrance channel. As in subsect. 4.2.1, it is easy to show that the resonance energy is given by

$$E_1^r - E_1 + \tilde{\gamma}_1^2 S_1(E_1^r) + \tilde{\gamma}_2^2 S_2(E_1^r) = 0, \qquad (4.3.35)$$

which generalizes (4.2.27) to two-channel systems. The observed widths read

$$\gamma_\alpha^2 = \tilde{\gamma}_\alpha^2/\left(1 + \tilde{\gamma}_1^2\,S_1'(E_1^r) + \tilde{\gamma}_2^2\,S_2'(E_1^r)\right), \qquad (4.3.36)$$

where S'_α is the energy derivative of S_α with respect to energy. Equations (4.3.35) and (4.3.36) provide the link between the experimental data $(E_1^r, \gamma_1^2, \gamma_2^2)$ and the R-matrix parameters $(E_1, \tilde{\gamma}_1^2, \tilde{\gamma}_2^2)$. This formalism is illustrated in the next subsections.

4.3.2   Example of Resonant Reaction: ^{3}He(d,p)^{4}He

The ^{3}He(d,p)^{4}He reaction presents a $3/2^+$ resonance near $E = 0.25$ MeV [71, 38]. The dominant angular momenta in the entrance and exit channels are therefore $\ell_i = 0$ and $\ell_f = 2$, respectively.

Table 4.2 *R-matrix parameters (in MeV) for the $^3He(d,p)^4He$ reaction. The observed reduced widths γ_d^2 and γ_p^2 correspond to $\Gamma_d = 0.026$ MeV and $\Gamma_p = 0.19$ MeV, respectively.*

	parameter	$a = 4$ fm	$a = 5$ fm
observed	E_1^r	0.210	0.210
	γ_d^2	0.147	0.098
	γ_p^2	0.038	0.027
formal	E_1	0.127	0.158
	$\tilde{\gamma}_d^2$	0.170	0.111
	$\tilde{\gamma}_p^2$	0.045	0.031

The cross section (2.5.45) is calculated with definition (4.33) of the collision matrix, using $a = 4$ fm, and 5 fm. The parameters are displayed in table 4.2 and the corresponding S-factors are given in fig. 4.3. In each case the following observed values have been adopted: $E^r = 0.21$ MeV, $\Gamma_d = 0.026$ MeV, $\Gamma_p = 0.19$ MeV. Near the resonance, the sensitivity of the S-factor to the R-matrix radius is very weak, but it reaches 10 % at zero energy. This is typical of the accuracy of the Breit-Wigner approximation far off resonance. Beyond 0.5 MeV, the fit underestimates the data since other partial waves, with $\ell_i > 0$, should be introduced.

4.3.3   Example of Non-Resonant Reaction: ^{6}Li(p,α)^{3}He

This reaction does not present any resonance at low energies. As was done in sect 4.2.3 for the phase shifts, a non-resonant transfer cross section can be fitted by a high-energy pole. This corresponds to a constant R-matrix. The S factor is presented in Fig. 4.4 for different a-values, and the R-matrix parameters are given in table 4.3. In the single-pole approximation, we have

$$R_{12}^2 = R_{11} \times R_{22}, \qquad (4.3.37)$$

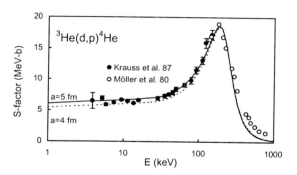

Figure 4.3.3: *R-matrix fit of the $^3He(d,p)^4He$ astrophysical factor. Experimental data are taken from references [38] and [71].*

and R_{12} is not a free parameter. Figure 4.4 shows that the sensitivity to a is very weak, and much lower than the experimental uncertainties. As discussed in subsect. 2.6.4, the experimental data are affected by electron screening below 100 keV. This atomic effect can not be accounted for by the R-matrix method, but the calculation provides estimates of the screening potential U_e [40].

Table 4.3 *R-matrix parameters for the $^6Li(p,\alpha)^3He$ cross section.*

a (fm)	R_{11}	R_{22}
4	0.40	0.25
5	0.77	0.06
6	0.80	0.03

4.4   Radiative-Capture Cross Sections

4.4.1   General Formalism

The determination of capture cross sections requires the calculation of matrix elements of the multipole operators. According to the R-matrix framework, such a matrix element between two wave functions Ψ_i and

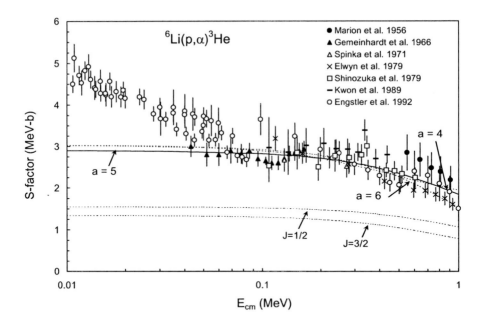

Figure 4.3.4:   R-matrix fit of the $^6Li(p,\alpha)^3He$ astrophysical S-factor
(taken from reference [40]). Dotted lines represent the individual contributions of the $1/2^+$ and $3/2^+$ partial waves, corresponding to $\ell_i = 0$.

Ψ_f is written as

$$< \Psi_f||\mathcal{M}_\lambda^\sigma||\Psi_i >=< \Psi_f||\mathcal{M}_\lambda^\sigma||\Psi_i >_{int} +$$
$$< \Psi_f||\mathcal{M}_\lambda^\sigma||\Psi_i >_{ext}= \mathcal{M}_{int} + \mathcal{M}_{ext}, \qquad (4.4.38)$$

where $\mathcal{M}_{int}$ and $\mathcal{M}_{ext}$ represent the internal and external contributions,
respectively. Using (2.4.41), the capture cross section can be rewritten as

$$\sigma_c = \frac{\pi}{k^2} \frac{2J_i + 1}{(2I_1 + 1)(2I_2 + 1)} |U^\gamma|^2, \qquad (4.4.39)$$

which extends the transfer cross section (2.5.45) to reactions involving
photons [15]. The "equivalent" collision matrix is divided in two parts

$$U^\gamma = U_{int}^\gamma + U_{ext}^\gamma. \qquad (4.4.40)$$

The internal part is determined with expansion (4.2.7) and definitions
(B.5) or (B.7) of amplitudes A_i (see eq.(4.2.7) and appendix B); U_{int}^γ can

be written in two ways:

$$U_{int}^\gamma = i^\ell \exp(i\delta_{HS}) \sum_{ij} (B^{-1})_{ij} \sqrt{\tilde{\Gamma}_i \tilde{\Gamma}_{\gamma,j}} \tag{4.4.41}$$

$$= i^\ell \exp(i\delta_{HS}) \frac{1}{1 - LR} \sum_i \frac{\sqrt{\tilde{\Gamma}_i \tilde{\Gamma}_{\gamma,j}}}{E_i - E} \tag{4.4.42}$$

where we have defined the gamma width of pole i as

$$\tilde{\Gamma}_{\gamma,i} = \frac{8\pi(\lambda + 1)k_\gamma^{2\lambda+1}}{\lambda(2\lambda + 1)!!^2} \frac{2J_f + 1}{2J_i + 1} |<\Psi_f||\mathcal{M}_\lambda^\sigma||\varphi_i>_{int}|^2. \tag{4.4.43}$$

The treatment of capture reactions therefore introduces new parameters: the gamma widths of the poles. As for particle widths, we make a distinction between formal and observed gamma widths (see next subsection).

The calculation of the external contribution is quite equivalent to the method developed in the potential model. We use the asymptotic forms (2.2.17) and (4.2.7) of the wave functions, which yields, for electric multipoles

$$\mathcal{M}_{ext} = eC_f F_E \int_a^\infty W_{-\eta_f,\ell_f+1/2}(2k_f\rho)$$
$$\left[I_{\ell_i}(k\rho) - U^{\ell_i} O_{\ell_i}(k\rho) \right] \rho^\lambda \, d\rho, \tag{4.4.44}$$

where C_f is the ANC of the final wave function, and F_E the geometric factor defined in sect. 3.3 for the potential model. A similar expression holds for magnetic multipoles. We have, for U_{ext}^γ,

$$U_{ext}^\gamma = i^{\ell+1} eC_f F_E \sqrt{\frac{2J_f + 1}{2J_i + 1} \frac{8\pi(\lambda + 1)k_\gamma^{2\lambda+1}}{\hbar v \lambda(2\lambda + 1)!!^2}}$$
$$\times \int_a^\infty W_{-\eta_f,\ell_f+1/2}(2k_f\rho)$$
$$\left[I_{\ell_i}(k\rho) - U^{\ell_i} O_{\ell_i}(k\rho) \right] \rho^\lambda \, d\rho. \tag{4.4.45}$$

This term is sometimes called "direct-capture contribution". Notice that the internal and external contributions are not independent of each other: the collision matrix U, occurring in the external term (4.4.45) involves the pole parameters which enter the internal term (4.41) or (4.42).

There is another derivation of U^γ. Expressing the collision matrix in the pole expansion provides for U_{ext}^γ a term similar to (4.4.42) where the γ widths are replaced by effective γ widths [62, 72], depending on the external contribution (see for example eq.(6) of ref.[62]). In this way, the remaining part of (4.4.45) does not depend anymore on the collision matrix. However, the γ widths become complex, with a phase depending on the pole. We do not develop this approach here.

Coming back to the phase between the internal and external components, it is interesting to mention that U^γ can be also written as

$$U^\gamma = i^\ell \exp(i(\delta_{HS} + \delta_R))(u_{int}^\gamma + u_{ext}^\gamma) \qquad (4.4.46)$$

where u_{int}^γ and u_{ext}^γ are *real* numbers. A simple algebraic manipulation gives

$$
\begin{aligned}
u_{int}^\gamma &= \frac{1}{|1 - LR|} \sum_i \frac{\sqrt{\tilde{\Gamma}_i \tilde{\Gamma}_{\gamma,i}}}{E_i - E} \\
u_{ext}^\gamma &= 2e C_f F_E \sqrt{\frac{2J_f + 1}{2J_i + 1} \frac{8\pi(\lambda + 1)k_\gamma^{2\lambda+1}}{\hbar v \lambda (2\lambda + 1)!!^2}} \\
&\quad \times \int_a^\infty W_{-\eta_f, \ell_f+1/2}(2k_f\rho) \left[F_{\ell_i}(k\rho) \cos(\delta_R) + \right. \\
&\quad \left. G_{\ell_i}(k\rho) \sin(\delta_R)\rho^\lambda \, d\rho. \right.
\end{aligned}
$$

$$(4.4.48)$$

which shows that the phase between external and internal terms is 0 or π. In most cases, the latter contribution is negligible if the capture occurs to deeply bound states, owing to the fast decrease of the Whittaker function. However, the external term must be calculated consistently with the internal term, i.e. with a phase shift determined from the same $\tilde{\Gamma}_i$ and E_i values. Also, the radius a must be identical.

4.4.2   Link between Observed and Formal Parameters

As for elastic scattering, parameters entering scattering cross sections are not directly related to observable data. When several poles are involved, the link between observed and formal parameters is not straightforward; an iterative method has been proposed in ref.[68]. When $N = 1$, observed parameters are defined by the Breit-Wigner parameterization

$$\sigma_c \approx \frac{\pi}{k^2} \frac{2J_i + 1}{(2I_1 + 1)(2I_2 + 1)} \frac{\Gamma_1 \Gamma_{\gamma,1}}{(E - E_1^r)^2 + \Gamma_1^2/4}, \qquad (4.4.49)$$

whereas eq.(4.4.39) provides the R-matrix expression with formal parameters

$$\sigma_c \approx \frac{\pi}{k^2} \frac{2J_i + 1}{(2I_1 + 1)(2I_2 + 1)} \frac{\tilde{\Gamma}_1 \tilde{\Gamma}_{\gamma,1}}{(E - E_1)^2 + L^2 \tilde{\gamma}^2}, \qquad (4.4.50)$$

where we have neglected the external contribution. Again, both definitions are equivalent provided that the relations (4.2.27) are satisfied and that the observed γ width is given by

$$\Gamma_{\gamma,1} = \tilde{\Gamma}_{\gamma,1}/(1 + \tilde{\gamma}_1^2 S'(E_1^r)). \qquad (4.4.51)$$

4.4.3 Examples

As in the potential model, we apply the R-matrix method to the $^7\mathrm{Be}(\mathrm{p},\gamma)^8\mathrm{B}$, $^3\mathrm{He}(\alpha,\gamma)^7\mathrm{Be}$, and $^{12}\mathrm{C}(\mathrm{p},\gamma)^{13}\mathrm{N}$ reactions, which represent typical examples of low-energy capture reactions. Again, we just aim here at illustrating the method, without trying to obtain optimal fits.

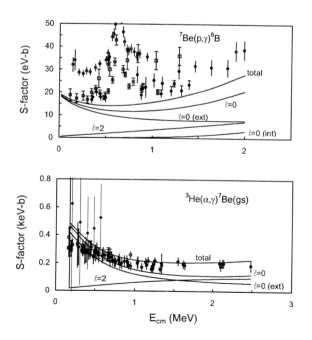

Figure 4.4.5: *R-matrix fits of the* $^7Be(p,\gamma)^8B$ *and* $^3He(\alpha,\gamma)^7Be$ *astrophysical factors ($3/2^-$ ground state only).*

Let us first discuss the non-resonant $^7\text{Be}(p,\gamma)^8\text{B}$ and $^3\text{He}(\alpha,\gamma)^7\text{Be}$ cross sections presented in fig. 4.5 with the parameters of table 4.4. In $^7\text{Be}(p,\gamma)^8\text{B}$, the external component, equivalent to the extranuclear-capture approximation, is accurate below 0.3 MeV, but underestimates the full calculation beyond this energy. The role of the short-range interaction is simulated by a pole, with an energy of 5 MeV (other choices are possible, provided that it is larger than 3 MeV). Its influence is obvious above 0.5 MeV, and represents the correction to the extranuclear approximation. With the $\ell = 2$ component (external only, since internal capture is negligible), the agreement with experiment is reasonable. Let us mention that the 1^+ resonance is not considered, and that we did not try to optimize the fit to the data.

For the $^3\text{He}(\alpha,\gamma)^7\text{Be}$ reaction, we only consider ground-state transitions. With an adequate choice of the ANC value, the data can be fairly well reproduced by external capture only. Introducing a high-energy pole (see table 4.4) slightly modifies the energy dependence. Above 1.5 MeV, the $\ell = 2$ partial wave represents the main contribution to the S-factor. Both examples show that the R-matrix method is also adapted to non-resonant reactions; a high-energy pole simulates the role of the internal region.

The $^{12}\text{C}(p,\gamma)^{13}\text{N}$ resonant reaction is illustrated in fig. 4.6 with the parameters of table 4.5. In a first step, the external component has been neglected ($C_f = 0$). In this way, experimental data can not be accurately reproduced by the single-pole Breit-Wigner approximation ($N = 1$), with the experimental parameters of the $1/2^+$ resonance at 0.42 MeV. Around zero energy, the calculation underestimates the data by a factor of two. This first approach can be improved in three ways:

1. Optimizing the R-matrix parameters (dotted line in fig. 4.6). With the parameters given in table 4.5, the low-energy S factor is improved, but the agreement near the resonance is less good.

2. Introducing a second pole at high energy ($N = 2$). We have chosen here $E_2 = 3$ MeV and the agreement with the data is significantly improved.

3. Introducing the external contribution. With $C_f = 0.96$ fm$^{-\frac{1}{2}}$ (see the lower panel of fig. 4.6), the agreement with the data is almost perfect down to zero energy. The calculation has been done for $a = 5$ fm and $a = 6$ fm. The (dominant) internal part is weakly sensitive to this choice, but the external correction varies by a factor

Table 4.4 *R-matrix parameters for the* $^7Be(p,\gamma)^8B$ *and* $^3He(\alpha,\gamma)^7Be$ *reactions. The radius is* $a = 5$ *fm.*

	^{7}Be(p,γ)^{8}B	^{3}He(α,γ)^{7}Be
$J_f^{\pi_f}$	2^+	$3/2^-$
E_f (MeV)	-0.137	-1.54
C_f (fm$^{-1/2}$)	0.75	6.0
Observed parameters		
E_1^r (MeV)	5.0	4.0
γ_1^2 (MeV)	0.49	0.02
$\Gamma_{\gamma,1}$ (eV)	60	80
Calculated parameters		
E_1 (MeV)	4.97	4.0
$\tilde{\gamma}_1^2$ (MeV)	0.49	0.02
$\tilde{\Gamma}_{\gamma,1}$ (eV)	60	80

of two. The resulting S-factor does not depend on a, as expected. This example illustrates the discussion of subsect. 4.4.1, where we showed that the cross section can be written as

$$\sigma = |\sqrt{\sigma_{int}} \pm \sqrt{\sigma_{ext}}|^2, \qquad (4.4.52)$$

with a real phase between the internal and external terms (+ for ^{12}C(p,γ)^{13}N). In a consistent calculation, the term σ_{ext} can not be called "direct capture" since it involves a resonant phase shift. This is well exemplified in fig. 4.6, where this external S-factor presents a resonant behaviour. This term not only depends on the phase shift, but also on the R-matrix radius. A better designation would be "correction to the Breit-Wigner approximation" (see subsect. 2.8).

4.5 Conclusion

The R-matrix method can be applied in many fields, and is the starting point of several approximations often used in low-energy nuclear physics

Table 4.5 *R-matrix parameters for the $^{12}C(p,\gamma)^{13}N$ reaction. The radius is $a = 6$ fm.*

	$N = 1$	$N = 1$ (opt)	$N = 2$
Observed parameters			
E^r (MeV)	0.420	0.416	0.420, 3.0
Γ_p (MeV)	0.033	0.032	0.033, 1.8
Γ_γ (eV)	0.5	0.9	0.5, 80
Calculated parameters			
E_1 (MeV)	-0.14	-0.15	$-0.31, 2.9$
$\tilde{\gamma}^2$ (MeV)	0.60	0.61	0.92, 0.51
$\tilde{\Gamma}_\gamma$ (eV)	0.82	1.5	2.4, 80

Table 4.6 *Approximations of the R-matrix method.*

Approximation	Comment
Elastic and transfer reactions	
N poles	General case
1 low-energy pole	Breit-Wigner approximation
1 high-energy pole	Non-resonant phase shift
Capture reactions	
N poles + external term	General case
1 low-energy pole without external term	Breit-Wigner approximation
1 high-energy pole without external term	Non-resonant cross section
External term only	Extranuclear approximation

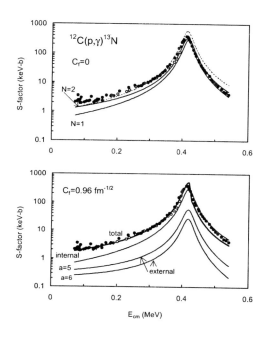

Figure 4.5.6: *R-matrix fits of the* $^{12}C(p,\gamma)^{13}N$ *astrophysical S-factor (see text). The internal components for* $a = 5$ *fm and* $a = 6$ *fm are undistinguishable.*

(see table 4.6). The Breit-Wigner approximation is a specific application of the R-matrix theory with a single pole, and without external correction. We have also shown with some examples that the R-matrix formalism can also be applied to non-resonant reactions, although very few cases have been considered in the literature. Finally, the well known extranuclear-capture model is also a peculiar adaptation of the R-matrix method, where the internal matrix elements of the multipole operators are completely neglected.

Chapter 5

Other Models used in Nuclear Astrophysics

5.1 Microscopic Cluster Models

5.1.1 Formalism

A microscopic model is based on basic principles of quantum mechanics, such as the treatment of all nucleons, with exact antisymmetrization of the wave functions. The hamiltonian of an A-nucleon system is

$$H = \sum_{i=1}^{A} T_i + \sum_{i<j=1}^{A} V_{ij}, \qquad (5.1.1)$$

where T_i is the kinetic energy and V_{ij} a nucleon-nucleon interaction [73, 74, 20, 21]. In microscopic cluster models, the wave function is written as

$$\Psi^{JM\pi} = \sum_{\alpha\ell I} \mathcal{A}\, g_{\alpha\ell I}^{J\pi}(\rho)\; \varphi_{\alpha\ell I}^{JM\pi}(\Omega_\rho, \boldsymbol{\xi}_1^i, \boldsymbol{\xi}_2^j), \qquad (5.1.2)$$

which corresponds to the Resonating Group (RGM) definition. This anzatz assumes that the A-nucleons are divided into two clusters with A_1 and A_2 nucleons. Index α corresponds to different two-cluster arrangements. In most applications, the internal cluster wave functions are defined in the shell model. Accordingly, the nucleon-nucleon interaction must be adapted to this choice, which leads to effective forces, such as the Volkov [75] or the Minnesota [76] interactions.

The main advantage of cluster models with respect to other micro-scopic theories is its ability to deal with reactions, as well as with nuclear spectroscopy. The first applications were done for reactions involving light nuclei, such as d, ^{3}He or α particles. More recently, much work has been devoted to the improvement of the internal wave functions: mul-ticluster descriptions [77, 78], large-basis shell model extensions [79], or monopolar distortion [80]. Microscopic cluster models have a wide range of applications, both in low-energy reactions and in the spectroscopy of light nuclei. The main limitation arises from the number of channels in-cluded in the wave function, which reduces the validity of the model at low energies. Also high-level densities require many channels in the wave functions. Nuclear astrophysics is probably one of the best candidates for applications of microscopic cluster models. The low energies and the low densities involved in most nuclei make the conditions of application quite valid. Many studies have been done in nuclear astrophysics [74, 20] but also in other fields, such as nucleus-nucleus bremsstrahlung [80], β decay to continuum [81] or spectroscopy of halo nuclei [21, 82].

5.1.2   Applications

We present here two applications of the RGM to nuclear astrophysics. We only focus on cross sections, but the method can also be used to determine spectroscopic properties relevant for astrophysics (resonance widths, transition probabilities, etc) [21]. The first reaction shown here is ^{7}Be(p,γ)^{8}B which has already been discussed in the potential-model and R-matrix frameworks. The second example deals with the ^{6}Li(p,α)^{3}He reaction which illustrates transfer reactions.

The ^{7}Be(p,γ)^{8}B cross section has been studied in a three-cluster model [77], where ^{7}Be is described by an $\alpha+^3$He structure. This ^{7}Be wave func-tion is suitable to reproduce its deformation. The model not only in-volves the ^{7}Be(3/2$^-$) ground state, but also the 1/2$^-$, 5/2$^-$ and 7/2$^-$ excited states which, as the ground state, can be fairly well described by an $\alpha+^3$He cluster structure. The ^{5}Li$+^3$He configuration, corresponding to an other arrangement of the α,^{3}He and p clusters, is also taken into account but plays a minor role. The resulting cross sections and spectro-scopic properties of ^{8}B and ^{8}Li are described in ref [77]. In fig. 5.1, we give the astrophysical S-factor obtained with four variants of the Volkov interaction [75]. It is well known [83] that this force overestimates the ANC of the ^{8}B ground state, but other microscopic calculations using the Minnesota force [76] also predict an $S(0)$ value larger than currently

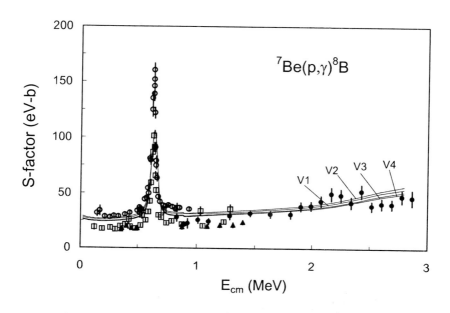

Figure 5.1.1: $^7Be(p,\gamma)^8B$ cross section for different Volkov potentials (taken from ref. [77]). The symbols follow the notations of Ref. [9].

accepted [9, 10]. Clearly the accuracy needed for this reaction [10] is beyond the scope of a microscopic model, which does not contain free parameters. On the contrary, the energy dependence is quite reliable and is used by many experimental groups to extrapolate their data down to zero energy (see for example ref. [84]).

Investigation of the ^{6}Li(p,α)^{3}He reaction is a part of an extended study of reactions involving 7 nucleons [86]. This work has been performed in a multicluster model, ^{6}Li being defined as α+p+n. Several channels, such as ^{6}Li(0$^+$)+p and ^{6}Be(0$^+$)+n are also included (see refs. [86, 87] for more detail). The main components to the cross sections arise from s waves, i.e. from $J = 1/2^+$ and $J = 3/2^+$. The corresponding phase shifts are shown in fig. 5.2, and compared with experimental data. The ^{6}Li(p,α)^{3}He S-factor is presented in fig. 5.3; the model does not include any screening effect, which is known to increase the data below 0.1 MeV (see subsect. 2.6.4). The order of magnitude of the data is well reproduced but the shape of the cross section is apparently in disagreement with experiment. Overestimation of the data has also been met in the similar ^{7}Li(p,α)^{4}He reaction [88]. The origin of the problem arises from the fact that a cluster description of ^{6}Li (or ^{7}Li) assumes that the α

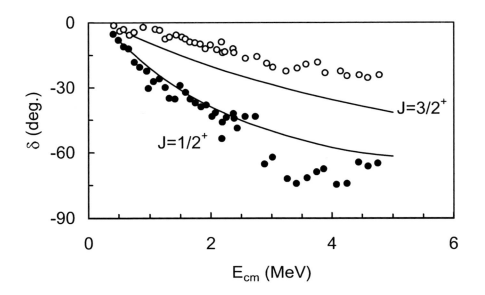

Figure 5.1.2: ^6Li+p *elastic phase shifts. The data are taken from ref. [85].*

wave function is identical to the wave function of a free α particle. This simplifying assumption is necessary, but makes the overlap between the $\alpha+^3$He and ^{6}Li+p channels too large. To illustrate this property, we have renormalized the RGM S-factor by 0.75 (dotted curve in fig. 5.3). This factor plays the role of a spectroscopic factor, and reduces the overlap between the initial and final channels. It makes the agreement with the data reasonable between 0.1 and 1 MeV. Below 1 MeV, the data are affected by electron screening, as mentioned before. Beyond 1 MeV, a $5/2^-$ resonance shows up in the data, but is not included in the model.

5.2 The Distorted Wave Born Approximation (DWBA)

The DWBA method can be applied to transfer reactions

$$a(=b+x) + A \rightarrow b + B\,(=A+x) \tag{5.2.3}$$

and assumes that particle x goes from the projectile a to the target A [89]. Let us consider the system (A, b, x) presented in fig. 5.4, and the

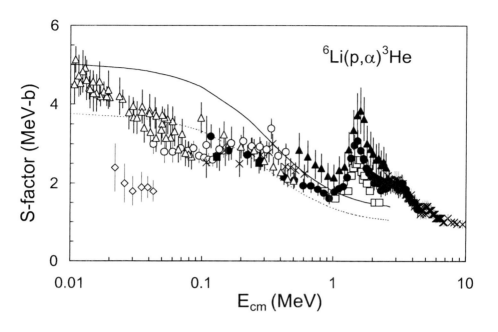

Figure 5.1.3: $^6Li(p,\alpha)^3He$ *S-factors without (full curve) and with (dotted curve) a renormalization factor 0.75 (see text). The symbols follow the notations of Ref. [9].*

different coordinates. The cross section for reaction (5.2.3) is obtained from matrix elements

$$T^{\mathrm{DWBA}} = \int \int d\boldsymbol{\rho}_\alpha d\boldsymbol{\rho}_\beta\, \chi_\beta^-(\boldsymbol{\rho}_\beta) < \Psi_b\Psi_B|\Delta V|\Psi_a\Psi_A > \chi_\alpha^+(\boldsymbol{\rho}_\alpha), \quad (5.2.4)$$

where the distorted waves $\chi_\alpha^+(\boldsymbol{\rho}_\alpha)$ and $\chi_\beta^-(\boldsymbol{\rho}_\beta)$, corresponding to the relative motion in the entrance and exit channels, respectively, are generated by optical potentials U_α and U_β. The residual interaction is defined in two different ways

$$\begin{aligned} \Delta V &= V_{xA} + V_{bA} - U_\alpha \quad \text{(prior)} \\ &= V_{bx} + V_{bA} - U_\beta \quad \text{(post)}, \end{aligned} \quad (5.2.5)$$

which correspond to "prior" and "post" definitions, respectively; they yield identical values for T^{DWBA}. The main problem of the method is that the potentials are usually poorly known. In general, a good approximation is to neglect $V_{bA} - U_\alpha$ or $V_{bA} - U_\beta$.

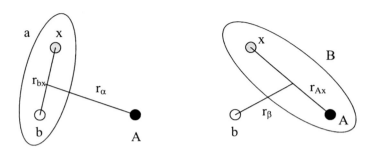

Figure 5.2.4: *Coordinate systems defining reaction (5.2.3).*

Since more realistic descriptions of nucleus a (B) should involve other configurations than $b+x$ $(A+x)$, spectroscopic factors are introduced ($\mathcal{S}_a$ and $\mathcal{S}_B$). The DWBA cross section is therefore linked to the experimental cross section through

$$\sigma_{\exp} = \mathcal{S}_a \, \mathcal{S}_B \, \sigma_{\text{DWBA}}. \tag{5.2.6}$$

A typical application is the $^7\mathrm{Li}(p,\alpha)^4\mathrm{He}$ reaction [90], shown in fig 5.5. The agreement with experiment is good but the large number of parameters makes the predictive power rather limited.

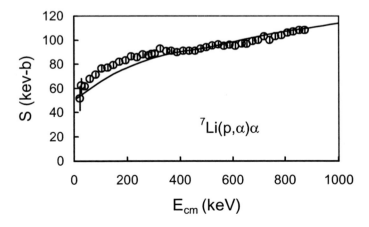

Figure 5.2.5: $^7Li(p,\alpha)^4He$ *cross section with the DWBA method [90].*

5.3 Indirect Methods

5.3.1 Coulomb Breakup

The Coulomb breakup method [91] is widely used in experiments using radioactive beams. The photodissociation reaction

$$c + \gamma \rightarrow a + b \qquad (5.3.7)$$

represents the reverse process of the capture reaction

$$a + b \rightarrow c + \gamma, \qquad (5.3.8)$$

and their cross sections σ_D and σ_C are related by the balance theorem

$$\sigma_D = \frac{(2I_a + 1)(2I_b + 1)}{2(2I_c + 1)} \frac{k^2}{k_\gamma^2} \sigma_C, \qquad (5.3.9)$$

where I_i represents the spin of nucleus i, k is the wave number associated with the $a + b$ system, and k_γ the wave number of the photon. In most applications, the photon wavelength is much larger than the $a + b$ wavelength, which means that

$$\frac{k^2}{k_\gamma^2} \gg 1, \qquad (5.3.10)$$

and σ_D is significantly larger than σ_C. This method is therefore a good way to compensate the smallness of capture cross sections at low energies.

In Coulomb breakup experiments [92, 93], nucleus C hits a heavy target which produces an intense field of virtual photons (see fig. 5.6). Assuming Coulomb excitation only, the excitation cross section reads

$$\frac{d\sigma}{d\Omega dE_\gamma} = \frac{1}{E_\gamma} \frac{dn}{d\Omega} \sigma_D, \qquad (5.3.11)$$

where Ω is the deflection angle, and $dn/d\Omega$ the number of virtual photons. This number makes cross section (5.3.11) large enough large enough to be measured in laboratory. It does not depend on the internal structure of the projectile, but on the kinematics of the relative motion.

The validity of (5.3.11) is essentially based on two conditions:

1. Excitation of projectile C is Coulombic only and nuclear effects are negligible.

2. "Post-acceleration" effects, i.e., modification of the $a + b$ energy
   after collision are negligible.

These conditions are in general satisfied for high incident energies and
small deflection angles. The first experiments have been performed with
the ^{6}Li$\rightarrow \alpha$+d breakup at 156 MeV [94]. They were essentially aimed at
testing the method. More recently, Coulomb breakup has been used with
radioactive beams, to investigate reactions such as ^{14}O$\rightarrow^{13}$N+p [95, 47]
or ^{8}B$\rightarrow^7$Be+p [96, 97].

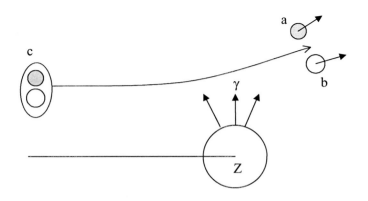

Figure 5.3.6: *Scheme of the photodissociation reaction.*

5.4   The ANC Method

As discussed in subsect.3.4.3, the main contribution to a capture cross
section involving weakly bound states arises from the asymptotic part
of the wave functions. A typical example is the ^{7}Be(p,γ)^{8}B reaction,
where the ^{8}B ground state is bound by 137 keV only. Figure 3.3 clearly
shows that the contribution of small relative distances is negligible in
the matrix elements. Of course, this is true at very low energies only
(typically $\leq$ 100 keV); for higher energies, the inner part of the wave
function and, consequently, the nuclear interaction, play a role.

When the external-capture approximation is valid, the cross section
to a final state f can be written as

$$\sigma_f(E) \approx |C_f|^2 \tilde{\sigma}_f(E), \tag{5.4.12}$$

where C_f is the asymptotic normalization constant (ANC), which represents the amplitude of the final wave function, and $\tilde{\sigma}_f(E)$ is independent of the model. The ANC method is based on transfer reactions where a nucleon of the projectile is transferred to the target. Energies must be large enough to ensure a peripheral process which is sensitive to the external part of the wave functions only. A recent example is the ${}^7\text{Be}({}^3\text{He,d}){}^8\text{B}$ reaction which has been used to determine the ANC of ${}^8\text{B}$ [98].

In the DWBA formalism [98, 60], the transfer cross section is directly proportional to $|C_f|^2$. The ANC methods seems almost "ideal" since the transfer cross sections are general known with a high accuracy. The problem is that the DWBA method is based on several approximations, and that the cross sections depend on potentials (in the previous example ${}^7\text{Be}+{}^3\text{He}$ and ${}^8\text{B}+\text{d}$) which are poorly known. The method seems to give results which weakly depend on the transfer reaction [99], but recent calculations on ${}^7\text{Be}(\text{p},\gamma){}^8\text{B}$ suggest that the uncertainties on the optical potential give an uncertainty of about 15% on $|C_f|^2$ [60].

5.5 Comments on Spectroscopic Factors

5.5.1 Definitions

The use of spectroscopic factors is widely spread in low energy nuclear physics. Intuitively, the spectroscopic factor aims at compensate neglected effects such as antisymmetrization or to simulate a more complex structure of the nucleus. Let us consider a system involving two nuclei (1 and 2) with wave functions $\Phi_1(\xi^1)$ and $\Phi_2(\xi^2)$ respectively (we follow the notations of sect. 2.2). If the total wave function is $\Psi^{\ell m}(\rho, \xi^1, \xi^2)$, the overlap integral [100] is defined as

$$\mathcal{I}_\ell(\rho) = < \phi_1(\xi^1)\, \phi_2(\xi^2)\, Y_\ell^m(\Omega_\rho)|\Psi^{\ell m}(\rho, \xi^1, \xi^2) >, \qquad (5.5.13)$$

where we have assumed that nuclei 1 and 2 have a spin zero. At large distances, $\mathcal{I}_\ell(\rho)$ tends to

$$\mathcal{I}_\ell(\rho) \longrightarrow C_\ell\, W_{-\eta, \ell + \frac{1}{2}}(2k_f\rho)/\rho, \qquad (5.5.14)$$

for bound systems.

The overlap integral can be expanded over a complete set of functions $\phi_{\ell n}(\rho)$ which defines the *spectroscopic amplitudes* $c_{\ell n}$ as

$$\mathcal{I}_\ell(\rho) = \sum_n c_{\ell n}\, \phi_{\ell n}(\rho). \qquad (5.5.15)$$

A possible basis is a set of harmonic oscillator functions [101]. In nuclear astrophysics, the expansion (5.5.15) is usually limited to a single term

$$\mathcal{I}_\ell(\rho) \approx c_{\ell 0}\, \phi_{\ell 0}(\rho), \tag{5.5.16}$$

where $\phi_{\ell 0}(\rho)$ is a radial function generated by an optical potential [60, 102, 49] which reproduces the binding energy. Approximation (5.5.16) is consistent with (5.5.14) but neglects short-range effects. Let us notice that, if $\Psi^{\ell m}$ is itself defined in the potential model, the spectroscopic amplitude $c_{\ell 0}$ is exactly unity.

From the overlap integral, one defines the *spectroscopic factor* [100] as

$$\begin{aligned}
\mathcal{S}_\ell &= \int_0^\infty |\mathcal{I}_\ell(\rho)|^2 \, \rho^2 \, d\rho \\
&= \sum_n |c_{\ell n}|^2.
\end{aligned} \tag{5.5.17}$$

Using approximation (5.5.16), we have

$$\mathcal{S}_\ell \approx |c_{\ell 0}|^2, \tag{5.5.18}$$

and the ANC constant reads

$$C_\ell \approx \sqrt{\mathcal{S}_\ell}\, b_\ell, \tag{5.5.19}$$

where b_ℓ is defined by the asymptotic behaviour of $\phi_{\ell 0}(\rho)$

$$\phi_{\ell 0}(\rho) \longrightarrow b_\ell\, W_{-\eta, \ell + \frac{1}{2}}(2k_f \rho)/\rho. \tag{5.5.20}$$

Indirect methods are usually based on a measurement of the spectroscopic factor $\mathcal{S}_\ell$. It should be kept in mind that definition (5.5.19) assumes that the expansion of $\mathcal{I}_\ell(\rho)$ is based on a single term. This approximation is valid only if the potential model can be applied. As we discussed in sect.3 this requirement is fulfilled in most light nuclei. However, if the set of states cannot be described by the potential model, eq. (5.5.16) is meaningless, and spectroscopic factors must be used very carefully.

5.5.2   Application to the DWBA Method

Our goal here is not to present the DWBA method in detail, but to point out its links with spectroscopic factors which, in turn, are used in nuclear astrophysics. We refer the reader to refs. [89, 100] for details. Let us consider reaction (5.2.3) with the coordinates of fig. 5.4. The DWBA transition amplitude reads

$$T_{\beta\alpha} = \int d\boldsymbol{\rho}_\alpha d\boldsymbol{\rho}_\beta \, \chi_\beta^-(\boldsymbol{\rho}_\beta)\mathcal{I}_{\beta\alpha}(\boldsymbol{\rho}_\alpha, \boldsymbol{\rho}_\beta)\chi_\alpha^+(\boldsymbol{\rho}_\alpha), \qquad (5.5.21)$$

where the overlap integral $\mathcal{I}_{\beta\alpha}$ is given by

$$\mathcal{I}_{\beta\alpha}(\boldsymbol{\rho}_\alpha, \boldsymbol{\rho}_\beta) = \int d\xi_A d\xi_b d\xi_x \Phi_B^*(\boldsymbol{\rho}_{Ax}, \xi_A, \xi_x)\Phi_b^*(\xi_b)$$
$$W(\boldsymbol{\rho}_\alpha, \boldsymbol{\rho}_\beta)\Phi_A(\xi_A)\Phi_a(\boldsymbol{\rho}_{bx}, \xi_b, \xi_x). \qquad (5.5.22)$$

The internal wave functions are denoted as Φ_i. We assume that interaction W does not depend upon the internal coordinates. Let us also note that the spin orientations have been disregarded in (5.5.22) for the sake of clarity.

To develop (5.5.22), let us expand the wave function Φ_B in a cluster basis involving A and x; we have

$$\Phi_B(\boldsymbol{\rho}_{Ax}, \xi_A, \xi_x) = \sum_* \Phi_A^*(\xi_A)\Phi_x^*(\xi_x)g_{Ax}^*(\boldsymbol{\rho}_{Ax}), \qquad (5.5.23)$$

where notation $(*)$ represents all quantum numbers (spin, isospin, etc). As in (5.5.16), this expansion is usually limited to a single term

$$\Phi_B(\boldsymbol{\rho}_{Ax}, \xi_A, \xi_x) \approx \sqrt{\mathcal{S}_{Ax}} \, \Phi_A(\xi_A)\Phi_x(\xi_x)R_{Ax}(\boldsymbol{\rho}_{Ax}), \qquad (5.5.24)$$

where $\mathcal{S}_{Ax}$ is the spectroscopic factor of nucleus B ($= A + x$) and R_{Ax} a radial function generated by an optical potential. With a similar approximation for Φ_a, the overlap integral becomes

$$\mathcal{I}_{\beta\alpha}(\boldsymbol{\rho}_\alpha, \boldsymbol{\rho}_\beta) \approx \sqrt{\mathcal{S}_{Ax}\mathcal{S}_{bx}} \, R_{Ax}(\boldsymbol{\rho}_{Ax})R_{bx}(\boldsymbol{\rho}_{bx})W(\boldsymbol{\rho}_\alpha, \boldsymbol{\rho}_\beta), \qquad (5.5.25)$$

where $\boldsymbol{\rho}_{Ax}$ and $\boldsymbol{\rho}_{bx}$ are expressed as a function of $\boldsymbol{\rho}_\alpha$ and $\boldsymbol{\rho}_\beta$. The cross section is therefore written as

$$\frac{d\sigma}{d\Omega} \sim |T_{\beta\alpha}|^2 \sim \mathcal{S}_{Ax}\mathcal{S}_{bx} \mid \int d\boldsymbol{\rho}_\alpha d\boldsymbol{\rho}_\beta$$
$$\chi_\beta^-(\boldsymbol{\rho}_\beta)R_{Ax}(\boldsymbol{\rho}_{Ax})R_{bx}(\boldsymbol{\rho}_{bx})W(\boldsymbol{\rho}_\alpha, \boldsymbol{\rho}_\beta)\chi_\alpha^+(\boldsymbol{\rho}_\alpha)|^2. \qquad (5.5.26)$$

Several comments should be done about this definition:

- The cross section is proportional to the product of the spectroscopic factors. This means that, in practice, one of them must be known. Besides, (5.5.26) is based on (5.5.24) which is in general valid for low-lying states of light nuclei, but which can be questioned for heavier systems.

- The formalism assumes that a and B are described by a single configuration since (5.5.24) involves one term only.

- The cross section is sensitive to the radial wave function of nuclei a and B. A multipole expansion of $T_{\beta\alpha}$ involves the orbital angular momenta of these systems [89]. This property is used to determine the spin of the nuclei, since the angular distribution (5.5.26) is sensitive to the angular momentum. This method has been used by Kubono et al. [103] to investigate the ^{20}Na spectrum through the ^{20}Ne(^{3}He,t)^{20}Na charge-exchange reaction. In this method, only the orbital momentum ℓ can be derived; assumptions must be made to determine the total spin J.

- Approximation (5.5.24) assumes that systems a and B are bound. Consequently the cross section (5.5.26) is not defined for resonant systems. In practice, if the lifetime of the resonance is long enough, (5.5.26) can be used.

- The DWBA method assumes from the very beginning that the transfer process (5.2.3) is non resonant. A possible resonant contribution must be removed from the data, which creates a further source of uncertainty.

- In addition to those limitations, it is important to keep in mind that all relative functions depend on poorly known (or not known at all) potentials. Consequently the DWBA must be used along with a careful analysis of the parameter sensitivity.

5.5.3   Use of Spectroscopic Factors in Nuclear Astrophysics

Spectroscopic factors are essentially used in two ways: calculation of capture cross sections and of resonance widths. Let us consider the capture reaction

$$a + b \rightarrow c + \gamma. \tag{5.5.27}$$

The cross section is given by a matrix element such as

$$\mathcal{M} = < \Psi_c(\boldsymbol{\rho}_{ab}, \boldsymbol{\xi}_a, \boldsymbol{\xi}_b) | \mathcal{M}_\lambda^E | \Phi_a(\boldsymbol{\xi}_a)\Phi_b(\boldsymbol{\xi}_b)g(\boldsymbol{\rho}_{ab}) >, \tag{5.5.28}$$

where $g(\boldsymbol{\rho}_{ab})$ is a scattering wave function, and Ψ_c represents the final wave function. Neglecting the internal contributions of the electric operator, we have

$$\mathcal{M} = \int \mathcal{I}_c(\boldsymbol{\rho}_{ab})\mathcal{M}_\lambda^E(\boldsymbol{\rho}_{ab})g(\boldsymbol{\rho}_{ab})d\boldsymbol{\rho}_{ab}, \qquad (5.5.29)$$

where $\mathcal{I}_c$ is the overlap integral introduced in 5.4.1, and $\mathcal{M}_\lambda^E(\boldsymbol{\rho}_{ab})$ is the radial part of the electric operator. Using approximation (5.5.16) provides

$$\mathcal{M} = \sqrt{\mathcal{S}_{ab}} \int \Phi_c(\boldsymbol{\rho}_{ab})\mathcal{M}_\lambda^E(\boldsymbol{\rho}_{ab})g(\boldsymbol{\rho}_{ab})d\boldsymbol{\rho}_{ab}, \qquad (5.5.30)$$

where Φ_c is generated by the potential model. Accordingly, the cross section is given by

$$\sigma_{\exp}(E) = \mathcal{S}_{ab}\,\sigma_{\mathrm{pot}}(E), \qquad (5.5.31)$$

where $\sigma_{\exp}(E)$ and $\sigma_{\mathrm{pot}}(E)$ are the experimental and theoretical cross sections, respectively [49].

Nuclear reaction rates also require resonance widths. At low energies, these resonances are very narrow and can not be measured directly. According to eq.(4.2.12) which provides the reduced width, we have

$$\gamma^2 \approx \mathcal{S}_{ab} \left(\frac{\hbar^2 a}{2\mu m_N} \right) |\Phi_c(a)|^2, \qquad (5.5.32)$$

which allows the width to be estimated from the spectroscopic factor [102].

Equations (5.5.31) and (5.5.32) are often used in nuclear astrophysics (see for example refs.[102, 104]), but one should keep in mind that these definitions are based on several assumptions which are difficult to evaluate.

Chapter 6

Reaction Rates

6.1 Introduction

As discussed in sect. 2, the reaction rate at temperature T is given by

$$N_A < \sigma v >= N_A \left(\frac{8}{\pi \mu m_N (k_B T)^3} \right)^{\frac{1}{2}}$$

$$\int S(E) \exp(-2\pi\eta - E/k_B T) \, dE, \qquad (6.1.1)$$

where we have introduced the S-factor. Rigorously the calculation should be performed numerically by using experimental or theoretical cross sections. However, an analytical approach provides a better understanding of the physics, and is still widely used. In addition, a numerical calculation for narrow resonances is not trivial. In the next subsections, we consider non-resonant and resonant rates separately, and compare analytical and numerical approaches.

Let us notice that we assume here a non-thermalized situation, where only the ground state of the colliding nuclei plays a role. This approximation is quite valid at low temperatures for light systems [8]. However if low-energy excited states are present (as in ^{19}F for example), these states can be populated and the reaction rate is modified. This problem will be briefly discussed in subsect. 6.4.3.

6.2 Non-Resonant Reaction Rates

In a non-resonant reaction, the S-factor weakly depends on energy. In this case, the integral (6.1.1) can be replaced by an accurate analytical approximation. In (6.1.1) the argument of the exponential presents a maximum at $E = E_0$, defined by (2.1.4). A Taylor expansion near E_0 gives

$$\exp(-2\pi\eta - E/k_B T) \approx \exp(-3E_0/k_B T)\exp\left(-\left(\frac{E - E_0}{\Delta E_0/2}\right)^2\right), (6.2.2)$$

E_0 and ΔE_0 defining the Gamow peak, where the cross section must be known to evaluate the reaction rate. Assuming $S(E) \approx S(E_0)$ in the Gamow peak, the reaction rate reads

$$N_A <\sigma v> \approx N_A \left(\frac{32E_0}{3\mu m_N (k_B T)^3}\right)^{\frac{1}{2}} \exp\left(-\frac{3E_0}{k_B T}\right) S(E_0), \qquad (6.2.3)$$

which presents a fast variation with temperature. A typical example is given in Fig. 6.1 with the $^3\mathrm{H}(\alpha,\gamma)^7\mathrm{Li}$ reaction [8]. Equation (6.2.3) involves two approximations:

- The S-factor is constant near E_0. If the variation is linear, $S(E_0)$ should be replaced by $S(E_0 + 5k_B T/6)$ in (6.2.3) [2].

- The Gaussian approximation (6.2.2) is used. A more accurate integration [2] yields an additional term $(1 + 5k_B T/36E_0)$.

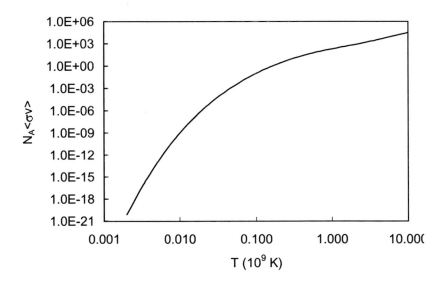

Figure 6.2.1: $^3H(\alpha,\gamma)^7Li$ reaction rate (in cm^3 $mole^{-1}$ s^{-1}) [8].

With those extensions, eq. (6.2.3) becomes

$$N_A < \sigma v > \approx N_A \left(\frac{32 E_0}{3 \mu m_N (k_B T)^3} \right)^{\frac{1}{2}}$$
$$\exp \left(-\frac{3 E_0}{k_B T} \right) S(E_0 + \frac{5}{6} k_B T) \left(1 + \frac{5 k_B T}{36 E_0} \right). \qquad (6.2.4)$$

Differences between (6.2.3) and (6.2.4) are small in general, but can be non-negligible at high temperatures.

The formalism developed here is valid for any form of the S-factor. The analytical procedure can be extended further by assuming a quadratic form of the S-factor

$$S(E) \approx S_0 + S_0' E + \frac{1}{2} S_0'' E^2, \qquad (6.2.5)$$

which is used in some astrophysics tables [8]. Let us mention that this approximation is in general valid for low energies only, i.e. for low temperatures. Using (6.2.5) in (6.2.4) provides

$$N_A < \sigma v > \approx N_A \left(\frac{32 E_0}{3 \mu m_N (k_B T)^3} \right)^{\frac{1}{2}} \exp(-\frac{3 E_0}{k_B T}) S_{eff}, \qquad (6.2.6)$$

where S_{eff} is given by

$$S_{eff} = S_0 (1 + \frac{5 k_B T}{36 E_0}) + S_0' (E_0 + \frac{35}{36} k_B T) +$$
$$\frac{1}{2} S_0'' E_0 (E_0 + \frac{89}{36} k_B T). \qquad (6.2.7)$$

This yields the well known [8] $T^{1/3}$ expansion of the reaction rate, up to $T^{5/3}$; eq.(6.2.7) provides the rate from the S-factor properties at zero energy.

Equation (6.2.7) is based on a quadratic expansion of the S-factor. In fig. 6.2, we present the ratio between the exact rate (computed numerically) and the approximate rate (computed with (6.2.7)) for the $^3\text{He}(\alpha,\gamma)^7\text{Be}$ and $^3\text{He}(d,p)^4\text{He}$ reactions. The former reaction is non-resonant and the S-factor is well approximated by a second order polynomial over a wide energy range. Hence, eq.(6.2.7) is very accurate. On the contrary, the $^3\text{He}(d,p)^4\text{He}$ reaction presents a broad resonance near 0.25 MeV (see fig. 4.3). Up to $T_9 \approx 1$, the E_0 values are in a range where the quadratic form is valid, and (6.2.7) is a good approximation. However, for $T_9 \geq 1$, E_0 is near the resonance energy, and (6.2.7) is meaningless.

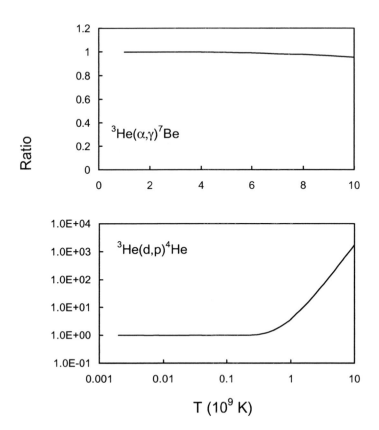

Figure 6.2.2: *Ratio between the exact reaction rate and the approximation (6.2.7).*

6.3 Resonant Reaction Rates

When the S-factor presents a Breit-Wigner form, the general definition (6.1.1) is of course still valid. However, one has to account for the fast variation of $S(E)$ near the resonance energy. Since a numerical approach is difficult for narrow resonances, we present an analytical method, widely used in nuclear astrophysics. A comparison between both approaches will be illustrated with the ^{12}C(p,γ)^{13}N reaction.

A careful analysis of integrand (6.1.1) shows that it always presents two maxima: at the resonance energy, and at the Gamow energy. This is illustrated in fig. 6.3 with the ^{12}C(p,γ)^{13}N reaction between $T_9 = 0.2$ and $T_9 = 0.3$. The peak at the resonance energy (0.42 MeV) does not depend on temperature. The second peak, corresponding to the Gamow energy, moves according to the temperature. From these considerations, and except in the temperature range where both peaks overlap, the resonant reaction rate can be split in two terms

$$N_A < \sigma v > \approx N_A < \sigma v >_R + N_A < \sigma v >_T, \qquad (6.3.8)$$

where $N_A < \sigma v >_R$ corresponds to the maximum at $E = E_R$. For a narrow resonance, we have

$$N_A < \sigma v >_R = N_A \left(\frac{2\pi}{\mu m_N k_B T}\right)^{\frac{3}{2}} \hbar^2 \omega\gamma \exp(-\frac{E_R}{k_B T}), \qquad (6.3.9)$$

where the resonance strength $\omega\gamma$ is defined by

$$\omega\gamma = \frac{2J+1}{(2I_1+1)(2I_2+1)} \frac{\Gamma_1\Gamma_2}{\Gamma_1+\Gamma_2}, \qquad (6.3.10)$$

J being the spin of the resonance, and (Γ_1, Γ_2) the widths in the entrance and exit channels. For a (p, γ) reaction at low energy, we have in general

$$\Gamma_\gamma \ll \Gamma_p, \qquad (6.3.11)$$

and therefore

$$\omega\gamma \approx \frac{2J+1}{(2I_1+1)(2I_2+1)} \Gamma_\gamma. \qquad (6.3.12)$$

The resonance strength is proportional to the lower partial width. The second maximum of integrand (6.1.1) yields the so-called "tail resonance" term $N_A < \sigma v >_T$. Its analytical expression is identical to the non-resonant rate (6.2.4) with a Breit-Wigner expression for $S(E)$.

As shown in fig. 6.3, the amplitudes of both peaks depend on temperature. In practice, except for temperatures where $E_0 \approx E_R$, a single term does contribute. Finally, let us notice that, if $E_0 \approx E_R$, decomposition (6.3.8) is not valid, and only a numerical integration can provide accurate results.

To illustrate the difference between the analytical and numerical approaches we present in table 6.1 the $^{12}C(p,\gamma)^{13}N$ reaction rate calculated with (6.3.8) and with a numerical approach. The calculation has been done for two R-matrix radii: $a = 5$ fm and $a = 6$ fm. At low temperatures, we have $E_0 \ll E_R$ (0.42 MeV) and (6.2.4) is dominant. The error is less than 17% compared with the numerical treatment. Let us notice that

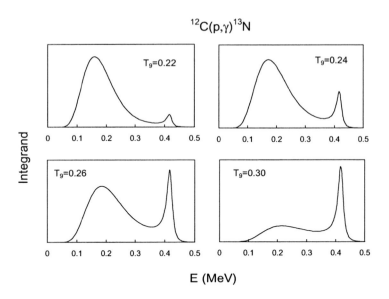

Figure 6.3.3: *Integrand of (6.1.1) for the $^{12}C(p,\gamma)^{13}N$ reaction at different temperatures.*

the Breit-Wigner approximation sensitively depends on the radius (about 10% here), which also affects the numerical rate. When temperature gets higher, the contribution of (6.3.9) becomes more important (see fig.6.3). The analytical approach remains accurate up to $T_9 \approx 0.5$, i.e. a temperature range covering most of the stellar scenarios involving $^{12}C(p,\gamma)^{13}N$. Beyond this temperature, the decomposition (6.3.8) is not valid, since the resonance tail (6.2.4) takes unphysically large values. This problem is solved by introducing [8] a "cut-off" temperature T_0 through a factor $\exp(-(T/T_0)^2)$ in (6.2.4). This factor cancels out the tail contribution above T_0 (here T_0 would be about 5×10^8 K). As shown by the numerical integration, only the resonant term remains.

Table 6.1 $^{12}C(p,\gamma)^{13}N$ reaction rate (in $cm^3\ mole^{-1}\ s^{-1}$). Bracketed numbers give the power of 10. The Gamow-peak energy E_0 is given in MeV. Errors provide the relative difference between the exact (numerical) calculation and approximation (6.3.8).

T_9	E_0		$a = 5$ fm				$a = 6$ fm		
		Exact	Eq.(6.2.4)	Eq.(6.3.9)	Error	Exact	Eq.(6.2.4)	Eq.(6.3.9)	Error
0.01	0.018	5.7(−20)	6.6(−20)	3.3(−204)	0.17	6.4(−20)	7.5(−20)	3.3(−204)	0.17
0.03	0.038	9.1(−12)	1.1(−11)	8.3(−64)	0.10	1.0(−11)	1.1(−11)	8.3(−64)	0.11
0.05	0.053	7.2(−9)	7.8(−9)	6.4(−36)	0.08	8.0(−9)	8.7(−9)	6.4(−36)	0.08
0.07	0.067	3.3(−7)	3.5(−7)	4.8(−24)	0.06	3.6(−7)	3.9(−7)	4.8(−24)	0.07
0.09	0.079	4.4(−6)	4.6(−6)	1.7(−17)	0.05	4.9(−6)	5.1(−6)	1.7(−17)	0.05
0.18	0.125	2.4(−3)	2.3(−3)	3.5(−6)	−0.04	2.6(−3)	2.5(−3)	3.5(−6)	−0.03
0.20	0.134	5.8(−3)	5.3(−3)	4.5(−5)	−0.07	6.2(−3)	5.8(−3)	4.5(−5)	−0.06
0.22	0.143	1.3(−2)	1.1(−2)	3.6(−4)	−0.10	1.4(−2)	1.2(−2)	3.6(−4)	−0.10
0.24	0.152	2.8(−2)	2.2(−2)	2.0(−3)	−0.13	3.0(−2)	2.4(−2)	2.0(−3)	−0.13
0.26	0.160	5.8(−2)	4.1(−2)	8.5(−3)	−0.16	6.2(−2)	4.4(−2)	8.5(−3)	−0.15
0.28	0.168	1.2(−1)	7.1(−2)	2.9(−2)	−0.16	1.2(−1)	7.6(−2)	2.9(−2)	−0.15
0.30	0.176	2.4(−1)	1.2(−1)	8.3(−2)	−0.14	2.5(−1)	1.3(−1)	8.3(−2)	−0.14
0.40	0.213	4.1	1.0	3.1	0.01	4.2	1.1	3.1	0.01
0.50	0.247	27.1	5.6	25.7	0.15	27.4	5.9	25.7	0.15

6.4   Other Processes

6.4.1   Neutron-Induced Reactions

For neutron-induced reactions, the low-energy cross section varies as

$$\sigma \sim \frac{1}{v}, \tag{6.4.13}$$

and the reaction rate (6.1.1) does not depend on temperature. This assumes s waves only, and the absence of resonances. For resonances, eq.(6.3.9) can be applied; partial waves with $\ell > 0$ provide some temperature dependence of the rate, but much weaker than for charged-particle induced reactions. Physical properties associated with neutrons and charged particles are therefore completely different.

6.4.2   Endoergic Reactions

For endoergic reactions, the threshold Q is negative, and the cross section is zero for $E \leq \mid Q \mid$. We have

$$\int_0^\infty \sigma(E)E \exp\left(-\frac{E}{k_B T}\right)$$
$$dE = \exp\left(-\frac{|Q|}{k_B T}\right)$$
$$\int_0^\infty \sigma(E + |Q|)(E + |Q|) \exp\left(-\frac{E}{k_B T}\right) dE, \tag{6.4.14}$$

and a factor $\exp(-|Q|/k_B T)$ shows up, which is small for large Q values. A typical example is the $^7\text{Li}(\alpha,\text{n})^{10}\text{B}$ reaction where $Q = -2.79$ MeV. Although a transfer cross section is expected to dominate the capture channel, the negative Q value makes the $^7\text{Li}(\alpha,\text{n})^{10}\text{B}$ reaction rate much lower than the $^7\text{Li}(\alpha,\gamma)^{11}\text{B}$ reaction rate.

6.4.3   Thermalization

As mentioned in subsect.6.1, some nuclei present excited states at low energy. In a stellar plasma, these states can be populated and the corresponding cross sections must be taken into account for calculating the rate. In such conditions, the reaction rate [8] reads

$$N_A < \sigma v >= N_A \frac{\sum_\alpha < \sigma_\alpha v > G_\alpha(T)}{\sum_\alpha G_\alpha(T)}, \tag{6.4.15}$$

where the partition function of a nucleus in its state α is given by

$$G_\alpha(T) = (2J_\alpha + 1) \exp(-\frac{E_\alpha}{k_B T}), \qquad (6.4.16)$$

E_α being the excitation energy.

To evaluate (6.4.15) the partial cross sections σ_α must be known. In general, the "equal strength" approximation is used, where all σ_α are assumed to be identical. The reaction rate (6.4.15) is then equal to the non-thermalized reaction rate. Other techniques [9] use the Hauser-Feshbach formalism to derive the ratio between thermalized and non-thermalized reaction rates.

Chapter 7

Conclusion

In this work, we have tried to give an overview of the theoretical problems involved in nuclear astrophysics. We were only concerned with reactions, without discussing other aspects, such as masses, beta decays, etc. In general, charged-particle induced reactions occur at energies much lower than the Coulomb barrier, and the corresponding cross sections are therefore extremely small. An other characteristic is that there is almost no systematics. In the low-mass region, each reaction presents its own peculiarities and difficulties, in the theoretical as well as in the experimental viewpoints. Nevertheless some hierarchy can be established among reactions of astrophysical interest. Transfer reactions, arising from the nuclear interaction, present cross sections larger than capture cross sections which have an electromagnetic origin. In addition, the resonant or non-resonant nature of a reaction also affects the cross section.

We have discussed different theoretical models often used in nuclear astrophysics. The potential model and the R-matrix method are widely applied in this field; they are fairly simple and well adapted to low-energy reactions. On the other hand, indirect methods are more and more developed since they overcome the major difficulty of nuclear astrophysics, i.e. the smallness of the cross sections. A very impressive amount of work has been devoted to nuclear astrophysics in the last decades. Although most reactions involving light nuclei are sufficiently known, some reactions, such as $^{12}C(\alpha, \gamma)^{16}O$ still require much effort to reach the accuracy needed for stellar models. In the nucleosynthesis of heavy elements (s process, p process), further problems arise from the level densities and the cross sections should be determined from statistical models. A better knowledge of these cross sections represents a challenge for the future.

I am grateful to Daniel Baye for many discussions about this topic, and to Carmen Angulo, Marianne Dufour, Pierre Leleux and Jeff Schweitzer for valuable comments about the manuscript.

Chapter 8

Appendix A

We give here formulas needed in the potential model for systems with non-zero spins. In the coordinate system defined in 3.1, the electromagnetic operators are written as

$$\mathcal{M}^\sigma_{\lambda\mu} = \mathcal{M}^\sigma_{\lambda\mu}(\rho) + \mathcal{M}^\sigma_{\lambda\mu}(\boldsymbol{\xi}^i_1) + \mathcal{M}^\sigma_{\lambda\mu}(\boldsymbol{\xi}^j_2), \tag{A.1}$$

where a relative term shows up as well as the internal moments of the nuclei. This equation is exact for $\lambda \leq 2$. For higher-order multipole, crossed terms may contribute.

We have to calculate the matrix elements of these three operators between wave functions (3.1.5) of the potential model. Using properties of the irreducible tensor operators, one gets for the radial term

$$
\begin{aligned}
< \Psi^{J_f \pi_f}_{\ell_f I_f} ||\mathcal{M}^E_\lambda(\rho)||\Psi^{J_i \pi_i}_{\ell_i I_i} > \; = \; & e\left(Z_1(\frac{A_2}{A})^\lambda + Z_2(-\frac{A_1}{A})^\lambda\right)(-1)^{\ell_i + J_i + I_i}\delta_{I_i I_f} \\
& \times \left[(2J_i + 1)(2\ell_f + 1)\right]^{1/2} < Y_{\ell_f}||Y_\lambda||Y_{\ell_i} > \\
& \times \left\{ \begin{matrix} J_i & J_f & \lambda \\ \ell_f & \ell_i & I_i \end{matrix} \right\} \int_0^\infty g^{J_f \pi_f}_{\ell_f I_f}(\rho)\rho^\lambda g^{J_i \pi_i}_{\ell_i I_i}(\rho)\,d\rho
\end{aligned}
\tag{A.2}
$$

where the matrix elements between spherical harmonics reads

$$< Y_{\ell_f}||Y_\lambda||Y_{\ell_i} > = < \ell_i\, 0\, \lambda\, 0|\ell_f\, 0 > \left[\frac{(2\lambda + 1)(2\ell_i + 1)}{4\pi(2\ell_f + 1)}\right]^{\frac{1}{2}}. \tag{A.3}$$

The matrix elements for the internal operators are obtained from

$$
\begin{aligned}
< \Psi^{J_f \pi_f}_{\ell_f I_f} ||\mathcal{M}^E_\lambda(\boldsymbol{\xi}^i_1)||\Psi^{J_i \pi_i}_{\ell_i I_i} > \; = \; & \delta_{\ell_i \ell_f}\left[(2J_i + 1)(2I_1 + 1)(2I_i + 1)(2I_f + 1)\right]^{\frac{1}{2}} \\
& \times (-1)^{I_1 + I_2 - J_f - \ell_f}\left\{ \begin{matrix} I_1 & I_2 & I_f \\ I_i & \lambda & I_1 \end{matrix} \right\}\left\{ \begin{matrix} J_i & J_f & \lambda \\ I_f & I_i & \ell_f \end{matrix} \right\} \\
& \times < \phi^{I_1}||\mathcal{M}^E_\lambda(\boldsymbol{\xi}^i_1)||\phi^{I_1} > \int_0^\infty g^{J_f \pi_f}_{\ell_f I_f}(\rho)\, g^{J_i \pi_i}_{\ell_i I_i}(\rho)\,d\rho
\end{aligned}
\tag{A.4}
$$

The matrix element for nucleus 2 is obtained by swapping I_1 and I_2. For $\lambda = 2$, the matrix element involves the quadrupole moment $Q(1)$, defined as

$$Q(1) = \sqrt{\frac{16\pi}{5}} < I_1 I_1 20 | I_1 I_1 > < \phi^{I_1} || \mathcal{M}_2^E(\boldsymbol{\xi}_1^i) || \phi^{I_1} >, \qquad (A.5)$$

which is different from zero only if $I_1 \geq 1$.

For magnetic multipoles $M1$, we have

$$< \Psi_{\ell_f I_f}^{J_f \pi_f} || \mathcal{M}_1^M(\boldsymbol{\rho}) || \Psi_{\ell_i I_i}^{J_i \pi_i} > = \mu_N \frac{Z_1 A_2^2 + Z_2 A_1^2}{A_1 A_2 (A_1 + A_2)}$$

$$[3\ell_i(\ell_i + 1)(2\ell_i + 1)(2J_i + 1)/4\pi]^{1/2} \delta_{\ell_i \ell_f} \delta_{I_i I_f}$$

$$\times (-1)^{\ell_i + J_i + I_i + 1} \left\{ \begin{array}{ccc} J_i & J_f & 1 \\ \ell_i & \ell_f & I_i \end{array} \right\} \int_0^\infty g_{\ell_f I_f}^{J_f \pi_f}(\rho)$$

$$g_{\ell_i I_i}^{J_i \pi_i}(\rho) \, d\rho, \qquad (A.6)$$

and

$$< \Psi_{\ell_f I_f}^{J_f \pi_f} || \mathcal{M}_1^M(\boldsymbol{\xi}_1^i) || \Psi_{\ell_i I_i}^{J_i \pi_i} > = \delta_{\ell_i \ell_f} \left[(2J_i + 1)(2I_1 + 1)(2I_i + 1)(2I_f + 1) \right]^{\frac{1}{2}}$$

$$\times (-1)^{I_1 + I_2 - J_f - \ell_f} \left\{ \begin{array}{ccc} I_1 & I_2 & I_f \\ I_i & 1 & I_1 \end{array} \right\} \left\{ \begin{array}{ccc} J_i & J_f & 1 \\ I_f & I_i & \ell_f \end{array} \right\}$$

$$\times < \phi^{I_1} || \mathcal{M}_1^M(\boldsymbol{\xi}_1^i) || \phi^{I_1} > \int_0^\infty g_{\ell_f I_f}^{J_f \pi_f}(\rho) \, g_{\ell_i I_i}^{J_i \pi_i}(\rho) \, d\rho, (A.7)$$

which involves the magnetic moment of nucleus 1

$$\mu(1) = \sqrt{\frac{4\pi}{3}} < I_1 I_1 10 | I_1 I_1 > < \phi^{I_1} || \mathcal{M}_1^M(\boldsymbol{\xi}_1^i) || \phi^{I_1} >, \qquad (A.8)$$

which is different from zero if $I_1 \geq 1/2$. It is possible to derive general formulas for magnetic multipoles, but those formulas are quite long and seldom used. We therefore limit ourselves to $\lambda = 1$.

Chapter 9

Appendix B

Here we briefly present the demonstration of some relations used in sect. 4, devoted to the R-matrix method. Let us first focus on eq.(4.2.15), by writing the inverse of matrix $\boldsymbol{B}$ (4.2.16) as

$$(B^{-1})_{ij} = \frac{\delta_{ij}}{(E_i - E)} + \frac{L\tilde{\gamma}_i\tilde{\gamma}_j}{(E_i - E)(E_j - E)b}, \qquad (\text{B.1})$$

where b is to be determined. Performing the product $\boldsymbol{B}^{-1}.\boldsymbol{B}$ yields

$$b = 1 - LR \qquad (\text{B.2})$$

where we have used (4.2.11). Then we have

$$\sum_{ij}(B^{-1})_{ij}\tilde{\gamma}_i\tilde{\gamma}_j = \frac{R}{1 - LR} \qquad (\text{B.3})$$

and eq. (4.2.15) is directly deduced by using (4.2.17).

To evaluate the capture cross section, let us express coefficients A_i (4.2.8) in two ways:

- First, we use definitions (4.2.7) for the radial wave function, and (4.2.11) for the R matrix. A direct calculation provides

$$g(a) = i^{\ell}\exp(i\delta_{\text{HS}})\sqrt{\frac{4\pi(2\ell + 1)aP}{kv}}\frac{R}{1 - LR}, \qquad (\text{B.4})$$

  which gives

$$A_i = i^{\ell}\exp(i\delta_{\text{HS}})\frac{1}{k}\frac{\sqrt{\pi\hbar(2\ell + 1)\tilde{\Gamma}_i}}{(1 - LR)(E_i - E)} \qquad (\text{B.5})$$

- In a second step, we establish from (B.1)

$$\sum_j (B^{-1})_{ij} \sqrt{\tilde{\Gamma}_j} = \frac{1}{1 - LR} \frac{\sqrt{\tilde{\Gamma}_j}}{E_i - E} \tag{B.6}$$

and coefficient A_i can be rewritten as

$$A_i = i^\ell \exp(i\delta_{\mathrm{HS}}) \frac{1}{k} \sqrt{\pi\hbar(2\ell + 1)} \sum_j (B^{-1})_{ij} \sqrt{\tilde{\Gamma}_j} \tag{B.7}$$

Bibliography

[1] F. Hoyle, *Mon. Not. R. Astron. Soc.* **106** (1946) 343

[2] D.D. Clayton, in *"Principles of stellar evolution and nucleosynthesis"*, The University of Chicago Press (1983)

[3] E.M. Burbidge, G.R. Burbidge, W.A. Fowler and F. Hoyle, *Rev. Mod. Phys.* **29** (1957) 547

[4] G. Wallerstein, I. Iben Jr., P. Parker, A.M. Boesgaard, G.M. Hale, A.E. Champagne, C.A. Barnes, F. Käppeler, V. Smith, R.D. Hoffman, F.X. Timmes, C. Sneden, R.N. Boyd, B.S. Meyer and D.L. Lambert, *Rev. Mod. Phys.* **69** (1997) 995

[5] F. Käppeler, F.-K. Thielemann and M. Wiescher, *Ann. Rev. Nucl. Part. Sc.* **48** (1998) 175

[6] M. Arnould and T. Takahashi, *Rep. Prog. Phys.* **62** (1999) 393

[7] F. Käppeler, *Prog. Part. Nucl. Phys.* **43** (1999) 419

[8] W.A. Fowler, G.R. Caughlan and B.A. Zimmerman, *Ann. Rev. Astron. Astrophys.* **5** (1967) 525; **13** (1975) 69
G.R. Caughlan and W.A. Fowler, *At. Data Nucl. Data Tables* **40** (1988) 283

[9] C. Angulo, M. Arnould, M. Rayet, P. Descouvemont, D. Baye, C. Leclercq-Willain, A. Coc, S. Barhoumi, P. Auger, C. Rolfs, R. Kunz, J.W. Hammer, A. Mayer, T. Paradellis, S. Kossionides, C. Chronidou, K. Spyrou, S. Degl'Innocenti, G. Fiorentini, B. Ricci, S. Zavatarelli, C. Providencia, H. Wolters, J. Soares, C. Grama, J. Rahighi, A. Shotter and M. Lamehi-Rachti, *Nucl. Phys.* **A656** (1999) 3

[10] E.G. Adelberger, S.M. Austin, J.N. Bahcall, A.B. Balantekin, G. Bogaert, L.S. Brown, L. Buchmann, F.E. Cecil, A.E. Champagne, L. de Braeckeleer, C.A. Duba, S.R. Elliot, S.J. Freedman, M. Gai, G. Goldring, C.R. Gould, A. Gruzinov, W.C. Haxton, K.M. Heeger, E. Henley, C.W. Johnson, M. Kamionkowski, R.W. Kavanagh, S.E. Koonin, K. Kubodera, K. Langanke, T. Motobayashi, V. Pandharipande, P. Parker, R.G.H. Robertson, C. Rolfs, F.F. Sawyer, N. Shaviv, T.D. Shoppa, K.A. Snover, E. Swanson, R.E. Tribble, S. Turck-Chièze and J.F. Wilkerson, *Rev. Mod. Phys.* **70** (1998) 1265

[11] C. Rolfs and W.S. Rodney, *Cauldrons in the Cosmos*, University of Chicago Press (1988)

[12] J. Vervier, *Prog. Part. Nucl. Phys.* **37** (1996) 435

[13] S. Kubono, *Prog. Theor. Phys.* **96** (1996) 275

[14] M.S. Smith and K.E. Rehm, *Ann. Rev. Nucl. Part. Sc.* **51** (2001) 91

[15] A.M. Lane and R.G. Thomas, *Rev. Mod. Phys.* **30** (1958) 257

[16] F.C. Barker, *Nucl. Phys.* **A575** (1994) 361

[17] J. Humblet, *Nucl. Phys.* **A187** (1972) 65

[18] V.I. Kukulin, V.G. Neudatchin, I.T. Obukhovski and Yu.F. Smirnov, in *"Clustering Phenomena in Nuclei"*, ed. K. Wildermuth and P. Kramer, Vieweg, Braunschweig (1983)

[19] D. Baye and P. Descouvemont, *Ann. Phys.* **165** (1985) 115

[20] K. Langanke, *Adv. in Nuclear Physics*, Vol. 21 (1994) p. 85

[21] P. Descouvemont, *Riken Review* **39** (2001) 102

[22] F.-K. Thielemann, M. Arnould and J.W. Truran, in *"Advances in Nuclear Astrophysics"*, eds. E. Vangioni-Flam et al. (1986) 525

[23] R.G. Newton, in *"Scattering Theory of Particles and Waves"*, Springer, New York, Heidelberg, Berlin (1982)

[24] M. Abramowitz and I.A. Stegun, *Handbook of Mathematical Functions*, Dover, London (1972) 1

[25] J. Humblet, *J. Math. Phys.* **26** (1985) 656

[26] D. Baye and E. Brainis, *Phys. Rev.* **C61** (2000) 025801

[27] H.J. Rose and D.M. Brink, *Rev. Mod. Phys.* **39** (1967) 306

[28] M. Kamionkowski and J.N. Bahcall, *Astrophys. J.* **420** (1994) 884

[29] J.N. Bahcall, S. Basu and M.H. Pinsonneault, *Phys. Lett.* **433B** (1998) 1

[30] P.E. Tegnér and C. Bargholtz, *Astrophys. J.* **272** (1983) 311

[31] R. Schiavilla, R.B. Wiringa, V.R. Pandharipande and J. Carlson, *Phys. Rev.* **C45** (1992) 2628

[32] J.N. Bahcall and P.I. Krastev, *Phys. Lett.* **436B** (1998) 243

[33] L.E. Marcucci, R. Schiavilla, M. Viviani, A. Kievsky and S. Rosati, *Phys. Rev.* **C63** (2001) 015801

[34] E.E. Salpeter, *Phys. Rev.* **88** (1952) 547; Astrophys. J. **115** (1952) 326

[35] J. Görres, H. Herndl, I.J. Thompson and M. Wiescher, *Phys. Rev.* **C52** (1995) 2231

[36] H. Dzitko, S. Turck-Chieze, P. Delbourgo-Salvador and C. Lagrange, *Astrophys. J.* **447** (1995) 428

[37] H.J. Assenbaum, K. Langanke and C. Rolfs, *Z. Phys.* **A327** (1987) 461

[38] A. Krauss, H.W. Becker, H.-P. Trautvetter, C. Rolfs and K. Brand, *Nucl. Phys.* **465** (1987) 150

[39] S. Engstler, G. Raimann, C. Angulo, U. Greife, C. Rolfs, U. Schröder, E. Somorjai, B. Kirch and K. Langanke, *Zeit. Phys.* **A342** (1992) 471

[40] C. Angulo and P. Descouvemont, *Nucl. Phys.* **A639** (1998) 733

[41] R. Bonetti, C. Broggini, L. Campajola, P. Corvisiero, A. D'Alessandro, M. Dessalvi, A. D'Onofrio, A. Fubini, G. Gervino, L. Gialanella, U. Greife, A. Guglielmetti, C. Gustavino, G. Imbriani, M. Junker, P. Prati, V. Roca, C. Rolfs, M. Romano, F. Schümann, F. Strieder, F. Terrasi, H.-P. Trautvetter and S. Zavatarelli, *Phys. Rev. Lett.* **82** (1999) 5205

[42] M. Lattuada, R. G. Pizzone, S. Typel, P. Figuera, D. Miljani, A. Musumarra, M.G. Pellegriti, C. Rolfs, C. Spitaleri, and H.H. Wolter, *Astrophys. J.* **562** (2001) 1076

[43] R.E. Azuma, L. Buchmann, F.C. Barker, C.A. Barnes, J.M. D'Auria, M. Dombsky, U. Giesen, K.P. Jackson, J.D. King, R.G. Korteling, P. McNeely, J. Powell, G. Roy, J. Vincent, T.R. Wang, S.S.M. Wong and P.R. Wrean, *Phys. Rev.* **C50** (1994) 1194

[44] C. Rolfs and R.E. Azuma, *Nucl. Phys.* **A227** (1974) 291

[45] P.B. Fernandez, E.G. Adelberger and A. Garcia, *Phys. Rev.* **C40** (1989) 1887

[46] P. Decrock, M. Gaelens, M. Huyse, G. Reusen, G. Vancraeynest, P. Van Duppen, J. Wauters, Th. Delbar, W. Galster, P. Leleux, I. Licot, E. Lienard, P. Lipnik, C. Michotte, J. Vervier and H. Oberhummer, *Phys. Rev.* **C48** (1993) 2057

[47] J. Kiener, A. Lefebvre, P. Aguer, C. O. Bacri, R. Bimbot, G. Bogaert, B. Borderie, F. Clapier, A. Coc, D. Disdier, S. Fortier, C. Grunberg, L. Kraus, I. Linck, G. Pasquier, M.-F. Rivet, F. St. Laurent, C. Stephan, L. Tassan-Got and J.-P. Thibaud, *Nucl. Phys.* **A552** (1993) 66

[48] T.A. Tombrello, *Nucl. Phys.* **71** (1965) 459

[49] C. Rolfs, *Nucl. Phys.* **A217** (1973) 29

[50] B. Buck, R.A. Baldock and J.A. Rubio, *J. Phys.* **G11** (1985) L11

[51] J. Raynal, in *"Computing as a Language of Physics"*, Trieste 1971, IAEA, Vienna (1972), p. 281

[52] M.J. Jamieson, *Comp. Phys. Comm.* **125** (2000) 193

[53] B. Buck, H. Friedrich and C. Wheatley, *Nucl. Phys.* **A275** (1977) 246

[54] D. Baye, *Phys. Rev. Lett.* **58** (1987) 2738

[55] S. Gartenhaus and C. Schwartz, *Phys. Rev.* **108** (1957) 482

[56] S. Typel, H.H. Wolter and G. Baur, *Nucl. Phys.* **A613** (1997) 147

[57] R.F. Christy and I. Duck, *Nucl. Phys.* **24** (1961) 89

[58] H.M. Xu, C.A. Gagliardi, R.E. Tribble, A.M. Mukhamedzhanov, and N.K. Timofeyuk, *Phys. Rev. Lett.* **73** (1994) 2027

[59] W. Liu, X. Bai, S. Zhou, Z. Ma, Z. Li, Y. Wang, A. Li, Z. Ma, B. Chen, X. Tang, Y. Han, and Q.Shen, *Phys. Rev. Lett.* **77** (1996) 611

[60] J.C. Fernandes, R. Crespo, F.M. Nunes and I.J. Thompson, *Phys. Rev.* **C59** (1999) 2865

[61] R.G. Thomas, *Phys. Rev.***88** (1952) 1109

[62] F.C. Barker and T. Kajino, *Aust. J. Phys.* **44** (1991) 369

[63] F.C. Barker and N. Ferdous, *Aust. J. Phys.* **33** (1980) 691

[64] F.C. Barker, *Phys. Lett.* **322B** (1994) 17;*Nucl. Phys.* **A609** (1996) 38

[65] F.C. Barker, *Phys. Rev.* **C53** (1996) 1449

[66] D. Baye and P. Descouvemont, *Nucl. Phys.* **A407** (1983) 77

[67] P.G. Burke, A. Hibbert and W.D. Robb, *J. Phys.* **B4** (1971) 153

[68] C. Angulo and P. Descouvemont, *Phys. Rev.* **C61** (2000) 064611

[69] P. Descouvemont, *Phys. Rev.* **C47** (1993) 210

[70] R.F. Barrett, B.A. Robson and W. Tobocman, *Rev. Mod. Phys.* **55** (1983) 155

[71] W. Möller and F. Besenbacher, *Nucl. Instr. Methods* **168** (1980) 111

[72] R.J. Holt, H.E. Jackson, R.M. Laszewski, J.E. Monahan and J.R. Specht, *Phys. Rev.* **C18** (1978) 1962

[73] K. Wildermuth and Y.C. Tang, *"A Unified Theory of the Nucleus"*, ed. by K. Wildermuth and P. Kramer, Vieweg, Braunschweig (1977)

[74] P. Descouvemont, *J. Phys.* **G19** (1993) S141

[75] A.B. Volkov, *Nucl. Phys.* **74** (1965) 33

[76] D.R. Thompson, M. LeMere and Y.C. Tang, *Nucl. Phys.* **A286** (1977) 53

[77] P. Descouvemont and D. Baye, *Nucl. Phys.* **A567** (1994) 341

[78] M. Dufour and P. Descouvemont, *Phys. Rev.* **C56** (1997) 1831

[79] P. Descouvemont, *Nucl. Phys.* **A584** (1995) 532

[80] D. Baye, P. Descouvemont and M. Kruglanski, *Nucl. Phys.* **A550** (1992) 250

[81] D. Baye and P. Descouvemont, *Nucl. Phys.* **A481** (1988) 445

[82] K. Varga, Y. Suzuki and R.G. Lovas, *Nucl. Phys.* **A571** (1994) 447

[83] D. Baye and N.K. Timofeyuk, *Phys. Lett.* **B293** (1992) 13

[84] F. Hammache, G. Bogaert, P. Aguer, C. Angulo, S. Barhoumi, L. Brillard, J.-F. Chemin, G. Claverie, A. Coc, M. Hussonnois, M. Jacotin, J. Kiener, A. Lefebvre, C. Le Naour, S. Ouichaoui, J.N. Scheurer, V. Tatischeff, J.-P. Thibaud, and E.Virassamynaiken, *Phys. Rev. Lett.* **86** (2001) 3985

[85] C. Petitjean, L. Brown and R.G. Seyler, *Nucl. Phys.* **A 129** (1969) 209

[86] K. Arai, D. Baye and P. Descouvemont, *Nucl. Phys.* **A699** (2002) 963

[87] K. Arai, P. Descouvemont and D. Baye, *Phys. Rev.* **C63** (2001) 044611

[88] P. Descouvemont and D. Baye, *Nucl. Phys.* **A 573** (1994) 28

[89] G.R. Satchler, in *"Direct Nuclear Reactions"*, Clarendon press, Oxford (1983)

[90] G. Raimann, B. Bach, K. Grün, H. Herndl, H. Oberhummer, S. Engstler, C. Rolfs, H. Abele, R. Neu and G. Staudt, *Phys. Lett.* **B249** (1990) 191

[91] G. Baur, K. Hencken, D. Trautmann, S. Typel and H.H. Wolters, *Prog. Part. Nucl. Phys.* **46** (2001) 99

[92] G. Baur, C.A. Bertulani and H. Rebel, *Nucl. Phys.* **A458** (1986) 188

[93] G. Baur and H. Rebel, *Ann. Rev. Nucl. Part. Sci.* **46** (1996) 321

[94] J. Kiener, H.J. Gils, H. Rebel, S. Zagromski, G. Gsottschneider, N. Heide, H. Jelitto, J. Wentz and G. Baur, *Phys. Rev.* **C44** (1991) 2195

[95] T. Motobayashi, T. Takei, S. Kox, C. Perrin, F. Merchez, D. Rebreyend, K. Ieki, H. Murakami, Y. Ando, N. Iwasa, M. Kurokawa, S. Shirato, J. Ruan (Gen), T. Ichihara, T. Kubo, N. Inabe, A. Goto, S. Kubono, S. Shimoura and M. Ishihara, *Phys. Lett.* **B264** (1991) 259

[96] T. Motobayashi, N. Iwasa, Y. Ando, M. Kurokawa, H. Murakami, J. Ruan (Gen), S. Shimoura, S. Shirato, N. Inabe, M. Ishihara, T. Kubo, Y. Watanabe, M. Gai, R.H. France III, K.I. Hahn, Z. Zhao, T. Nakamura, T. Teranishi, Y. Futami, K. Furutaka and T. Delbar, *Phys. Rev. Lett.* **73** (1994) 2680

[97] T. Kikuchi, T. Motobayashi, N. Iwasa, Y. Ando, M. Kurokawa, S. Moriya, H. Murakami, T. Nishio, J. Ruan, S. Shirato, S. Shimoura, T. Uchibori, Y. Yanagisawa, T. Kubo, H. Sakurai, T. Teranishi, Y. Watanabe, M. Ishihara, M. Hirai, T. Nakamura, S. Kubono, M. Gai, R.H. France III, K. I. Hahn, T. Delbar, P. Lipnik and C. Michotte, *Eur. Phys. J.* **A3** (1998) 213

[98] A.M. Mukhamedzhanov, R.E. Tribble and N.K. Timofeyuk, *Phys. Rev.* **C51** (1995) 3472

[99] J.C. Fernandes, R. Crespo and F.M. Nunes, *Phys. Rev.***C61** (2000) 064616

[100] D.F. Jackson, in *"Clustering Phenomena in Nuclei"* , ed. K. Wildermuth and P. Kramer, Vieweg, Braunschweig (1983)

[101] M. Ichimura, A. Arima, E.C. Halbert and T. Terasawa, *Nucl. Phys.* **A204** (1973) 225

[102] C. Iliadis, *Nucl. Phys.* **A618** (1997) 166

[103] S. Kubono, N. Ikeda, M. Yasue, T. Nomura, Y. Fuchi, H. Kawashima, S. Kato, H. Orihara, T. Shinozuka, H. Ohnuma, H. Miyatake and T. Shimoda, *Z. Phys.* **A331** (1988) 359

[104] C. Iliadis, P.M. Endt, N. Prantzos and W.J. Thompson, *Astrophys. J.* **524** (1999) 434

Index

A

angular momentum, 5, 10, 18, 23, 34, 66
asymptotic normalization constant (ANC), 6, 31, 47, 50, 56, 62-64
atoms, 15

B

binding energy, 26, 64
Breit-Wigner approximation, 20, 38, 43, 50-53, 74

C

capture cross sections, 79
capture reactions, ix, 4, 8, 17, 47, 49
cluster models, 55, 56
clusters, 55, 56
CNO cycle, ix
colliding nuclei, 4, 43, 69
Coulomb barrier, 1, 4, 79
Coulomb breakup, ix, 61, 62
Coulomb functions, 2, 6, 14, 22, 35
Coulomb potential, 5, 22
cross sections, ix, 1, 2, 4, 6, 8, 11, 17-20, 25, 28, 29, 33, 45, 48, 50, 56, 57, 61, 63, 66, 69, 76, 77, 79, 80

E

endoergic reactions, 76

G

Gaussian potential, 23, 26, 27

H

Hauser-Feshbach theory, 2
He burning, ix
heavy elements, 1, 14, 79

I

internal spins, 24, 25

L

low energy, 29, 39, 63, 73

M

microscopic cluster models, 55, 56
microscopic models, ix, 1, 23